Revised
Digital Communication II
Laboratory Manual

Edited by Mohamad Tavakoli

Learning Solutions

New York Boston San Francisco
London Toronto Sydney Tokyo Singapore Madrid
Mexico City Munich Paris Cape Town Hong Kong Montreal

www.pearsonhighered.com

ISBN 10: 0-558-42057-5
ISBN 13: 978-0-558-42057-4

CONTENTS

Lab Exercise 4—Satellite Earth Station Transmitter

Lab Exercise 5—Satellite Transponder System

Lab Exercise 6—Satellite Earth Station Receiver System

Lab Exercise 7—BPSK Signals Generation

Lab Exercise 8—BPSK Signals Multiple Access

Lab Exercise 9—BPSK Signals Recovery

Lab Exercise 10—QPSK Modulator

Lab Exercise 11—QPSK Demodulation

Lab Exercise 12—QAM Modulator Design with Different Constellations

Lab Exercise 13—Generation of PN Codes with a Modulo Shift Register

Lab Exercise 14—Generation of PN Codes with a Simple Shift Register

Lab Exercise 15—Changing the Initial Values for a PN Code Generator

Lab Exercise 16—PN Codes: Study of Shift-and-Add Property

Lab Exercise 17—Baseband DSSS Transmitting and Receiving Systems

Lab Exercise 18—BPSK DSSS Transmitting and Receiving Systems

Glossary

Bibliography

Index

Appendix

About this Edition

In order to make the lab simulations easier for the students, the following changes have been made in the lab manual:

1. Figures have been redrawn and enlarged to make them readable.
2. The location of each block in the library has been provided.
3. The parameters of each block have been added.
4. More detailed description of the simulation has been provided for each lab.
5. The parameters for running the simulation properties have been included.

In the newer version of VisSim software, several blocks were modified to use an external "clock" pulse to improve the efficiency of the simulation. For these modified blocks the output clock of the source that produces the data should be connected to the input clocks of these units in order for the simulation to work without any problems.

All comments are welcome and are hereby gratefully acknowledged,

Mohamad Tavakoli
ITT Technical Institute
5005 South Wendler Drive
Tempe, AZ 85282
Email: mtavakoli@itt-tech.edu

Conventions Used in the Book

This book contains features such as notes, tips, warnings, and references, identified by various icons. Each of these icons presents a different type of information. Following is the list of icons that will be used in the book.

A note provides information about the topic in context. This is additional information related to the topic.

A tip provides an alternative method for performing a task. It can also contain a simplified, although unconventional, method of doing a task.

Just-a-Minute presents nice-to-know information or a quick question that checks the learners' understanding of the current topic.

A warning informs you about the dire effects of an action. Focusing on these warnings reduces the likelihood that learners will make the same errors.

A reference provides links to Web sites or relevant books and white papers for further study on a particular topic.

Each topic begins with objectives that inform learners about the learning outcome of a topic.

All colored figures in the book have been marked with an asterick sign. These colored figures are available in the Appendix for reference.

Lab Exercise 1—DPSK Modulation and Demodulation

Objective

- Study the generation of differential binary signal.
- Study the differential PSK modulation.
- Study the differential PSK demodulation.

Theory

Carrier and Bit Clock Generator

IC8038 is a basic waveform generator that generates sine, square, and triangular waveforms. The sine wave generated by the IC8038 is used as carrier signal to the system. The square wave generated by IC8038 is at the 12V level. So this is converted into a +5V signal with the help of a transistor (2N3904 or BC107) and diode (OA79 or IN4148). Figure 1.01 shows a carrier and bit clock generator.

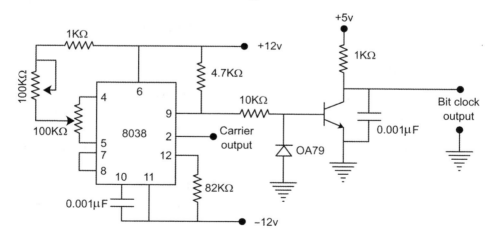

Figure 1.01: Carrier and Bit Clock Generator

Data Generator

The square wave is used as a clock input to a decade counter (IC7490), which generates the modulating data outputs. Figure 1.02 shows a data generator.

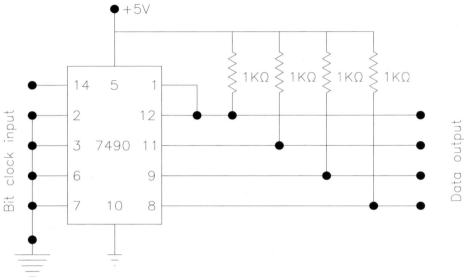

Figure 1.02: Data Generator

Modulation

The differential signal to the modulating signal is generated using an EX-OR gate and a 1-bit delay circuit. CD4051 is an analog multiplexer to which the carrier is applied, with and without the 180° phase shift (created by using LM741 op-amp connected in inverting amplifier mode) to the two inputs of the CD4051. A differential signal generated by EX-OR gate (¼ IC7486) is given to the multiplexer's control signal input. Depending on the level of the control signal, a carrier signal applied with or without PSK is steered to the output. 1-bit delay generation of differential signal to the input is created by using a D-flip flop (½ IC7474).

A -5 V for the IC CD4051 can be generated by using a zener diode 1N751 (5.1 V) with the cathode connected to ground and anode connected through a 1.5 ohms resistor to -12 V.

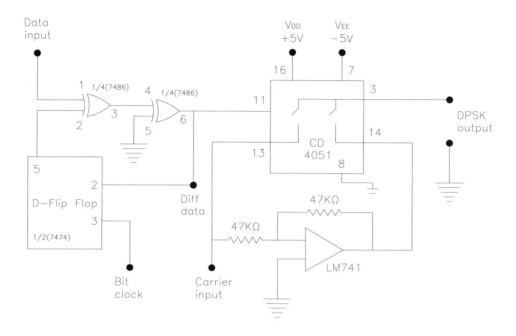

Figure 1.03: DPSK Modulator

Demodulation

During demodulation, the DPSK signal is converted into a +5V square wave signal using a transistor and is applied to one input of an EX-OR gate. To the second input of the gate, carrier signal is applied after conversion into a +5V signal. So the EX-OR gate output is equivalent to the differential signal of the modulating data. This differential data is applied to one input of an EX-OR gate and so for the second input, after a 1-bit delay, the same signal is given. The output of this EX-OR gate is a modulating signal.

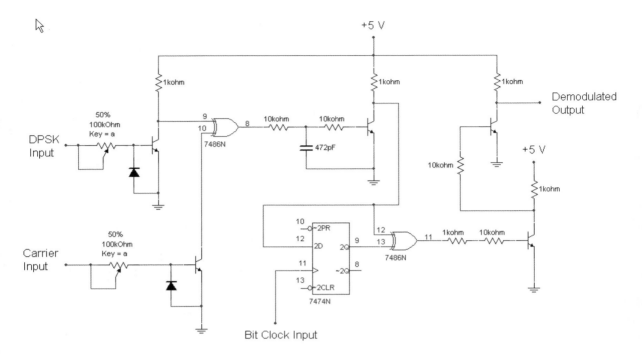

Figure 1.04: DPSK Demodulator

Problem Statement

Study differential PSK modulation and demodulation.

Lab Setup

- Oscilloscope
- Probes and connecting wires

DPSK Parts-S. No.	Part Description
1	IC7490
2	IC8038
3	CD4051

4	IC7474 and IC7486
5	BC107/ 2N3242 npn transistors
6	OA79 diodes* or IN4148
7	1 KΩ
8	10 KΩ
9	47 KΩ
10	4.7 KΩ
11	100 K pots
12	82 KΩ
13	0.001 μF
14	500 pF
15	LM324 or LM741 Op Amp

Table 1.1: DPSK Components

Type	Maximum Inverse Voltage Peak	Average	Maximum Forward Current Peak	Average
OA79	45v	30v	100ma	4ma

Table 1.2: Specifications for OA79 Diode

Procedure

1. Switch the experimental board on.

2. Check the carrier signal and the data generators signals.

3. Apply the carrier signal to the carrier input of the DPSK modulator and give the data generator to the data input of the DPSK modulator and bit clock output to the input of DPSK modulator.

4. Observe the DPSK modulating output with respect to the input data generator signal of dual trace oscilloscope (observe the DPSK modulating signal on channel 1 and the data generator signal on channel 2).

5. Give the output of the DPSK modulating signal to the input of the demodulator. Give the bit clock output to the bit clock input to the demodulator. Give the carrier output to the carrier input of demodulator.

6. Observe the demodulator output with respect to the data generator signal (modulating signal).

Conclusion/Observation

1. Differential PSK modulation and demodulation are observed.
2. Is there any similarity in operation between DPCM and DPSK?
3. What is the advantage of DPSK over BPSK?

Lab Activity Checklist

S. No.	Tasks	Completed	
		Yes	No
1.	Observed the operation of the bit clock generator and carrier generator		
2.	Observed differential PSK modulation		
3.	Observed differential PSK demodulation		

Lab Exercise 2—Multipath Delay Distortion

Objective

- Simulate an FSK modulated multipath wireless communications channel.

- Vary the number of paths and discover and report the number of paths at which minimum multipath delay distortion occurs.

- Vary delay factor and record and report the delay at which maximum similarity occurs.

Lab Setup

PC with Commsim simulator

Text Reference

Tomasi—Chapter covering Microwave Radio Communications and System Gain— Line-of-sight Path Characteristics.

Theory

Multipath occurs when the transmitted signal follows more than one travelling path. These signals arrive at the receiver input at different time intervals because they have travelled different distances. When the signals arrive in phase, the combined signal amplitude increases. When the signals arrive out of phase, the signal amplitude decreases and cause fading.

Problem Statements

- Record the appropriate value of the number of paths at which the minimum distortion occurs.
- Vary the delay factor and record the effect on the demodulated output at the receiver and record the appropriate delay at which the maximum similarity occur.

Circuit Diagram (in Commsim)

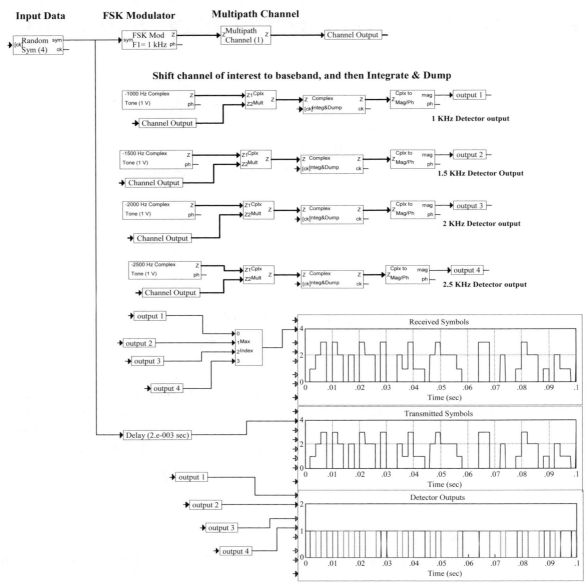

*Figure 2.01: Multipath channel simulation

Procedures

1. Construct the circuit of Figure 2.01. Insert a random symbol generator (Comm> Signal Sources) as input data and set it as follows:

    Internal clock mode   Number of symbols: 4

    Symbol Rate: 500   Start time: 0

    The number of symbols is four for 4-ary FSK input.

2. Add an FSK modulator (Comm> Modulator) and set it to 1 kHz. The FSK modulator is configured for 4-ary output, with 1KHz as the lowest tone and 500 Hz spacing between tones. The four tones are 1, 1.5, 2 and 2.5 KHz.

3. Insert a multipath channel (Comm> Channel Category) from the Commsim window and connect it as indicated in the circuit diagram. Set the parameters as follows:

    Initial condition: 0   Delay Mode: Seconds

Number of Paths: You can choose up to four paths and the amount of weight and phase rotation of each path.

4. In order to avoid crowded wiring, use variable block (Blocks> Annotation> Variable) and name them properly. As an example in this figure a variable with the name of "Channel Output" is used and you can use this variable with the same name in other places in the diagram without connecting them via the wire.

5. In order to recover the symbols four detectors are used. In each of these detectors the following units are needed.

    a) Multiplication of the FSK signal with proper carrier. Since the output of the FSK modulator is complex, four complex tone generators are needed as shown in Figure 2.01. The complex tone (Comm/Signal Sources) connected to the Z1 input of complex multiplier (Comm> Complex Math). The other input of the multiplier Z2 is connected to Z output of the Multipath channel.

    b) The output of the multiplier is connected to the complex integrate and dump (Comm> Operators) unit. The complex integrator and damp continuously integrate the input signal and periodically dumped and reset to a specified value for symbol recovery. Set the parameters of this unit as follows:

    Reset value: 0   Scale factor: 500   Dump Timing: Internal

    Output Mode: Hold   Dump rate: 500   Integration method: Euler

c) In order to show the output on the plot a complex to magnitude and phase (Comm> Complex Math) unit is used. The magnitude output of this unit is connected to one of the inputs of the plot.

6. The largest output value among these four integrators is the demodulated symbol.

Therefore in order to detect the FSK signal, the outputs of the complex to magnitude blocks are connected to the inputs of the maximum index block (Comm> Operators> Max index). This block returns the index of the largest input signal. The block can be configured to accept up to 16 inputs. A typical application of this block is in the creation of M-ary decision circuits (e.g. detection of MFSK). Should two or more inputs share the largest value, the output index will be that of the lowest input connection in the set. Set the parameters of this block as follows:

Number of inputs: 4   Index Mode: Starts at zero

7. Insert a real delay function (Comm> Operators) as indicated in the diagram and set the delay to 2e-0.003 seconds. The delay is used because of the delay in integrator and dump unit to make input and the output in the same time frame for comparison purposes.

8. Run the simulation under the following properties:

a) Choose Simulate > Simulation Properties

b) Click on the Range tab

c) Set Frequency to 20,000 and End to 0.1

9. Observe multipath effects, particularly and the delay between transmitted and received signals.

10. Vary the number of multipath channels and observe changes in effects.

11. Vary the amount of delay in the delay function and attempt to achieve maximum similarity.

12. For an extra exercise, in Commsim, these detectors can be constructed as compound blocks. The compound blocks are used to avoid crowded figure and wiring. This is shown in Figure 2.02.

The following procedure shows how to create a compound block:

a) Select the blocks to be encapsulated.

b) Choose Edit > Create Compound Block

c)   Under compound name, enter a name (e.g. 1 KHz Detector). Avoid using the dot (.) character in the name. Commsim uses it to separate compound block names in the title bar. The default name is compound.

d)   Click on the OK button, or press Enter.

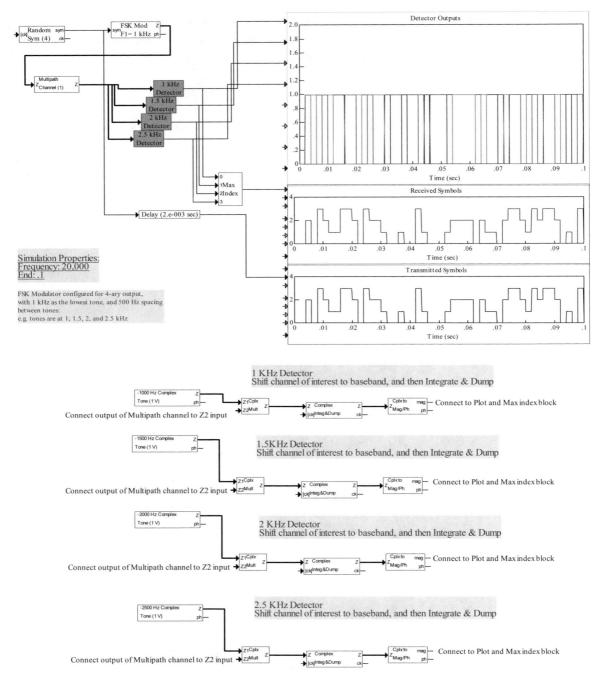

*Figure 2.02: Multipath Channel simulation using Compound Blocks

Conclusions/Observations

1. Describe the effect on the demodulated signal of varying the number of multipath channels:

2. Describe the effect of varying the delay. Did you achieve maximum similarity? If so, at what value of delay?

Lab Exercise 3—Simulated Wireless Path with Interference

Objective

- Simulate wireless propagation between a transmitter and receiver.
- Inject an interference signal and report intermodulation distortion products.

Lab Setup

PC with Commsim simulator

Text Reference

Tomasi—Chapter covering Microwave Radio Communications and System Gain—Line-of-sight Path Characteristics.

Theory

Multipath affects signals propagating through both wireless and fiber optic. In wireless systems, radio waves can take alternate paths from the transmitter to the receiver. For example, in line-of-site systems there is the direct wave from the transmit antenna to the receive antenna. There can also be alternate paths in which the radio wave will bounce off buildings or water. In fiber optic systems, we have multimode, where the signal generated from a single laser can take alternate paths through the fiber. In all cases, this can have a negative effect on the performance of the communications network. Interfering signals can also have an effect on both wireless and fiber optic networks. In most cases, interfering signals can be filtered out at the front end of the receiver. However, there are harmonic products and inter-modulation products that can be generated within the bandwidth of the receiver. Inter-modulation products are somewhat similar to harmonics however; they are generated by two signals operating at different frequencies.

Problem Statement

Use Commsim to simulate a communications circuit operating at 2 MHz. Inject signals at the receiving antenna to simulate both multipath and interfering signals, and to investigate the effect they have on performance. Measure the effect the interfering signals have on the primary signal, and observe the inter-modulation products that are generated.

Procedures

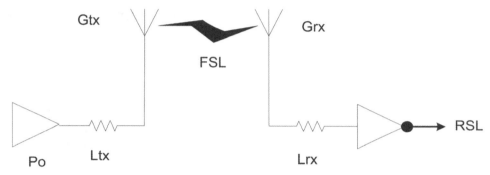

Figure 3.01: A wireless system

1. Construct the wireless system of Figure 3.01 using Commsim, and use the following parameter settings:

Po = 6 dBm: Output power of the transmitter

Ltx = 1.5 dB: Transmitter feeder loss

Gtx = 3 dB: Transmitter antenna gain

Grx = 3 dB: Receiver antenna gain

Lrx = 2 dB: Receiver feeder loss

FSL: Free space loss based on a 10-mile link

Receiver gain: 50 dB

2MHz sinusoidal signal source

The block diagram shown in Figure 3.01 describes the components required. It is better to search through the various blocks available in Commsim and come up with your own design schematic.

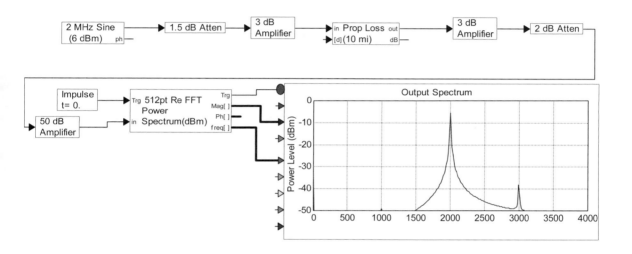

*Figure 3.02: Simulation layout of Figure 3.01

2. Set up the circuit as shown in Figure 3.02. Use the blocks in Figure 3.02 as follows:

    a) Sine Source: (Comm> Signal Sources)

    Frequency: 2MHz,   Output power: 6dBm

    b) Attenuator: (Comm> RF> Attenuator dB). This block implements a passive RF attenuator.

    c) Amplifier: (Comm> RF> Amplifier). This block implements a nonlinear RF amplifier. Block parameters include the amplifier small signal gain, the 1 dB compression point, second and third order intermodulation (IM) intercept points, and the amplifier noise figure. The block can also be modelled as a noiseless device. 50 Ohm impedance is assumed. Use it with the default values.

    d) Propagation Loss (Comm> Channels). Set the following properties:

        Path distance (mi): 10

        Frequency (MHz): 2

        Distance Mode: Internal

        Distance Unit: miles

    e) Spectrum analyzer real: (Comm> Operators)

        Trigger mode: Trigger

        Spectral Output: Mag/Phase

        FFT window type: Rectangular

        FFT size: 512

        Power Spectrum Unit: dBm

        Load: 50 ohms

        Output Frequency: KHz

    f) Display: (Display tab)

        External trigger: 0;

        XY Plot X axis: 4

        Fixed Axis

        Y-upper: 0   Y-Lower: -50

        X-upper: 4000   X-lower: 0

3.   Use the following simulation properties: (Simulation> Simulation properties)

        Frequency: 7000,000 Hz

        End: 0.01

Run the simulation using the initial settings shown above, and record spectral information

4.   Measure RSL (Received Signal Level) with a spectrum analyzer function using the plot and compare it with your calculation.

5.   Refer to Figure 3.03 and inject a 2 MHz signal at –60 dBm and zero phase shift, at the receiving antenna to simulate interference. Use a sine source and an RF combiner for this purpose. The RF combiner can be found in Comm> RF> Splitter or combiner.

6.   Record the difference in spectrum on both the primary and harmonic frequencies.

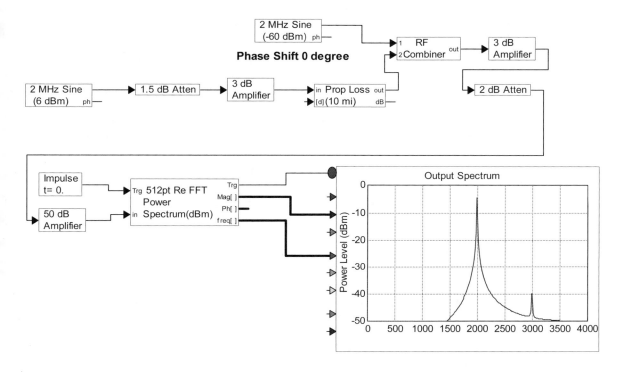

*Figure 3.03: Injecting signal in receiving antenna to simulate interference effect

7. Change the phase shift of the interference signal to 180 degrees and record amplitudes of primary and harmonics.

8. Change the phase back to zero degrees. Then change the frequency of the interference signal to 2.5 MHz. Record frequency and signal amplitudes for each peak in the spectrum.

Conclusion/Observation

In conclusion, the designer wants to ensure an adequate receive signal level to maintain the expected BER, or better. However, just taking into account all the gains and losses in a network may not be adequate to determine if enough margin is available. The designer also needs to consider the effects of multipath and interfering signals. As demonstrated, a multipath signal can either add to, or decrease from, the primary signal. In practice, a multipath signal will do both at different instances in time. We need to take into account worse conditions so the designer needs to assume even that, at times, the signal will be 180 degrees out of phase. Therefore, the designer will have to take this into account in added margin required for the signal-to-noise ratio. The negative effect of multipath can be compensated for by either more gain in the network or by diversity. There are three primary forms of diversity used, including space, frequency, and polarization. Space diversity is most commonly used in radio networks. In that case, two antennas are separated by at least one-half of the wavelength of the frequency in use. The output is combined and the stronger signal is selected. If the antennas are adequately separated, chances are that when one signal fades the other will add the reflected signal. It turns out that two systems operating on different frequencies will do the same. It is said that primary and reflected signals are frequency selective. Polarization diversity is used in a variety of systems. It works on the same concept as frequency diversity, but instead uses different antennas with different polarization.

1. Refer to recorded observations and describe the effect on received spectrum of phase shift (vs. no phase shift) of an interference signal.

2. Refer to recorded observations and describe the effects on received spectrum of an interference signal of a slightly but noticeably different frequency of interference signal.

Lab Exercise 4—Satellite Earth Station Transmitter

Objective

- Simulate satellite earth station transmitter system in Commsim.
- Observe and analyze the signals at different blocks of the satellite earth station transmitter system.

Lab Setup

PC with Commsim simulator

Theory

The earth station transmitter for a satellite communication system is shown in the following figure. The original baseband signal is first BPSK modulated. The output of the BPSK modulator is passed through a bandpass filter to remove any out-of-band harmonics and noise. The signal is then up-converted to high frequency, usually 6GHz or 14GHz. These are the common uplink frequencies used. Once again, the output of the up-converter is passed through a bandpass filter centered around the up-converter frequency. The output from the bandpass filter is then given to the high-power amplifier which provides the necessary high powers required in satellite communications. The output of the high-power amplifier is sent into the channel using an antenna system.

Figure 4.01 shows a satellite earth station transmitter.

Simulation Properties:
Frequency: 100
End: 40

Bandpass filter

31 PN Sequence [ck] out ck

Baseband Signal

Bilevel, Bit rate: .25
Internal

*

BPSK Modulation

1 Hz Sine
(1 V) ph

6th Order 0.5 - 1.5 Hz
Butterworth Bandpass

Comm>Filters>IIR

6th Order 4.5 - 7.5 Hz
Butterworth Bandpass

*

6 Hz Sine
(1 V) ph

High power amplifier

5

Signal to sattelite transponder

Transmitter output

8
6
4
2
0
-2
-4
-6

0   5   10   15   20   25   30   35   40
Time (sec)

Trg 512pt Re FFT
Power Spectral
in Density(dBm/Hz)

Trg
Mag[ ]
Ph[ ]
freq[ ]

Transmitter output spectrum

25
20
15
10
5
0
-5
-10
-15
-20

0   5   10   15   20   25

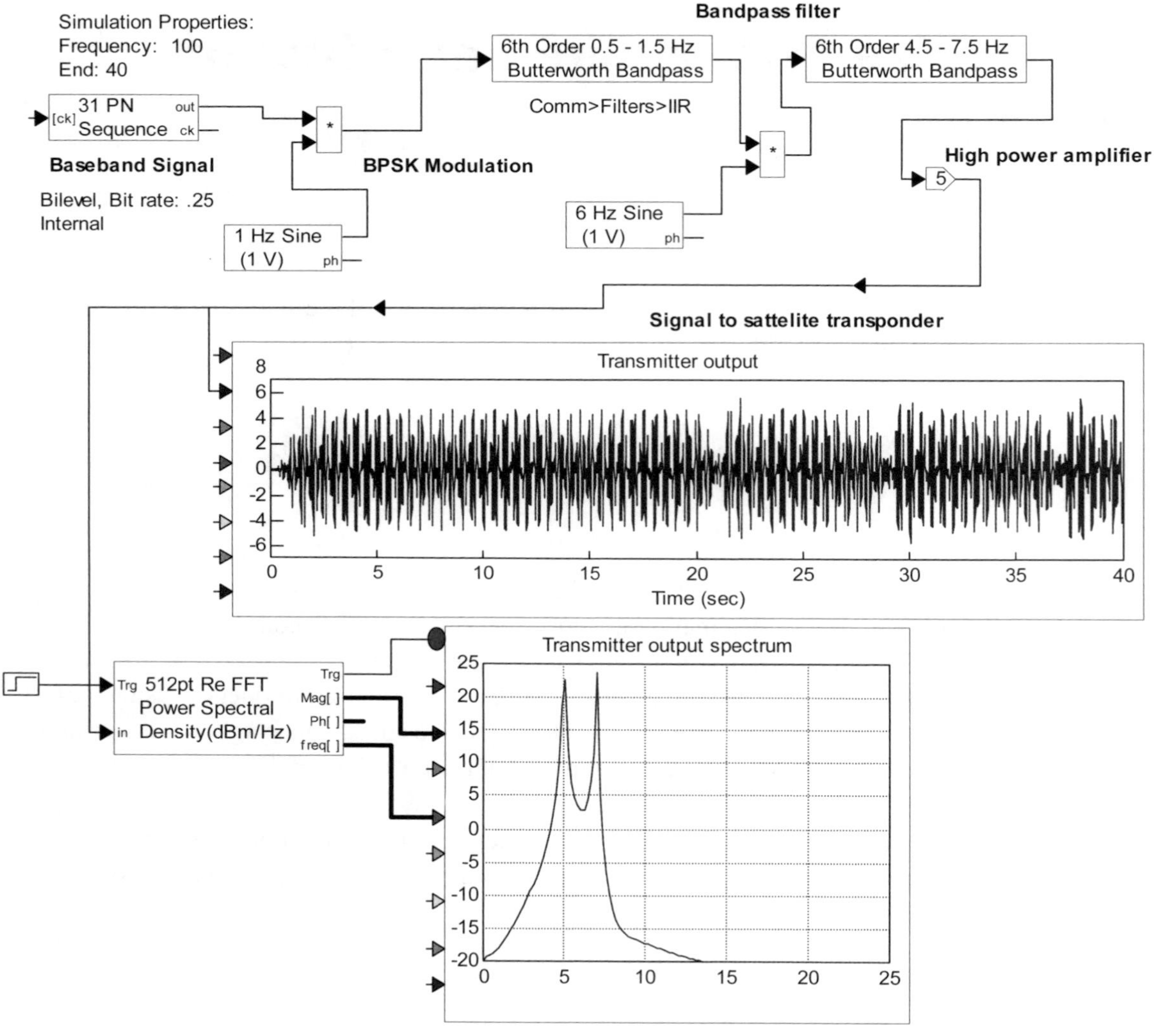

*Figure 4.01: Satellite Earth Station Transmitter

Problem Statement

Simulate and study the satellite earth station transmitter.

Procedure

1. Set up the circuit as shown in Figure 4.01.

2. Use a PN sequence (Comm> Signal sources) code generator as the digital baseband signal generator. Set up the bit rate of the PN code generator as 0.25 bps. Set the signal level to bi-level and clock to internal.

3. Use a 1Hz sinusoid signal (Comm> Signal sources) as the BPSK carrier.

4. Use a multiplier (Blocks> Arithmetic) as BPSK modulator.

5. Since the output of the BPSK signal will be centered around 1Hz, use a bandpass filter centered around 1Hz. You may also use a low-pass filter with cutoff at 2Hz as the carrier is of very low frequency in the simulation. In original systems the frequency of the BPSK carrier will be of the order of MHz.

6. Use a 6th order Butterworth bandpass filter (Comm> Filters> IIR). Set the lower frequency of the filter 0.5Hz and the upper frequency to 1.5Hz.

7. Use a 6Hz sinusoid as the up-converter frequency. In real-life systems a frequency of 6GHz or 14GHz is used as uplink center frequency.

8. Use a 6th order Butterworth bandpass filter centered around 6Hz as the bandpass filter after the up-conversion. Set the lower frequency to 4.5Hz and upper frequency to 7.5Hz. This will remove frequencies that fall out of band especially the harmonics.

9. A simple gain block (Blocks> Arithmetic) is used as the high-power amplifier. Set the gain to 5.

10. The output of the amplifier is the actual output of the ground station earth transmitting system that is sent down the channel, which is nothing but free space LOS channel to the satellite transponder.

11. Connect the output of the gain block to spectrum analyzer unit. Set the following for this unit:

> Spectrum analyzer real: (Comm> Operators)
>> Trigger mode: Trigger
>> Spectral Output: Mag/Phase
>> FFT window type: Rectangular
>> FFT size: 512
>> Power Spectrum Unit: dBm/Hz
>> Load: 50 ohms
>>> Output Frequency: Hz

12. Connect the Spectrum analyzer block to display. Use the following setting for this unit:

External trigger: 0;

XY Plot X=axis: 4

13. Use the following simulation properties (Simulate> Simulation Properties):

Frequency: 100Hz

End: 40

Run the simulation using the initial settings shown above, and record spectral information.

14. Use a display plot to study output of different blocks of the transmitter and trace the signal.

Conclusion/Observation

1. The signals at different blocks of the satellite earth station transmitting system are observed and analyzed.

2. What happens if the frequency of the BPSK modulating carrier is close to the up-converter frequency?

3. In realistic systems, where do you think the BPSK carrier and the up-converter find themselves in the frequency spectrum?

4. What will the effect of increasing the order for the Butterworth filter?

Solution Graphs

Figure 4.02 shows the actual baseband digital signal at 0.25 bps. The corresponding spectrum of this baseband signal is also shown in Figure 4.03.

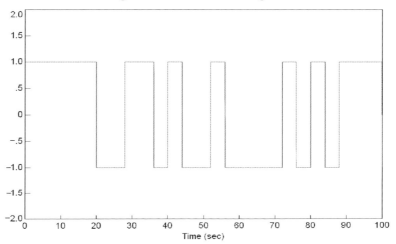

Figure 4.02: Baseband Digital Signal

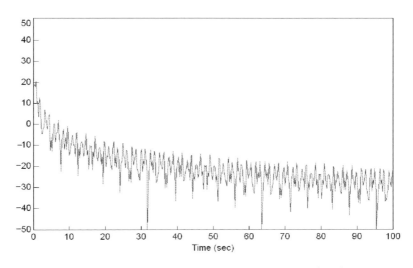

Figure 4.03: Spectrum of Baseband Digital Signal

The spectrum of the baseband digital signal is observed to be centered at the zero frequency as the frequency of the signal is very low.

Figure 4.04 shows the BPSK carrier and its frequency spectrum.

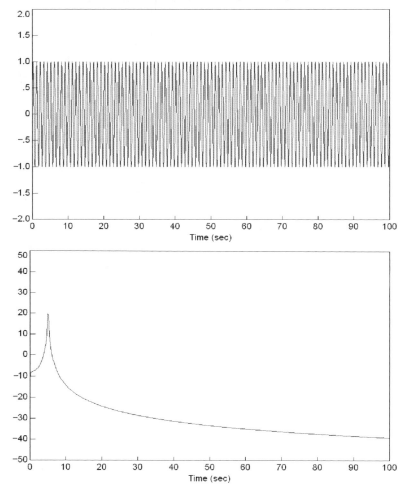

Figure 4.04: BPSK Carrier and its Spectrum

Figure 4.05 shows the BPSK modulated output, where you may observe the phase reversal at bit value transition.

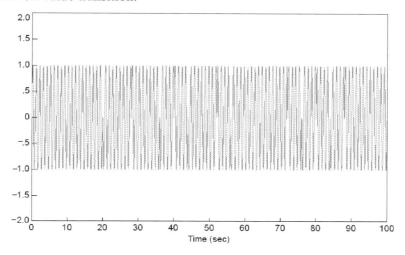

Figure 4.05: BPSK Output

Figure 4.06 shows the spectrum of the BPSK output. The spectrum is now centered at the BPSK carrier frequency.

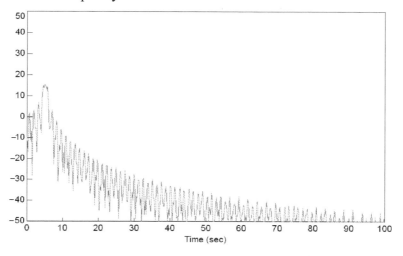

Figure 4.06: Spectrum of BPSK Output

Figures 4.07 and 4.08 show the output of the first bandpass filter and its spectrum.

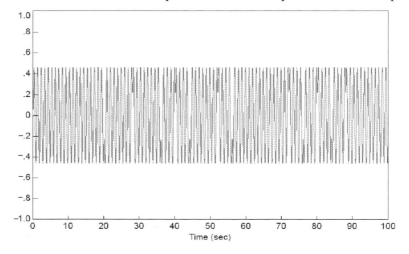

Figure 4.07: First Bandpass Filter Output

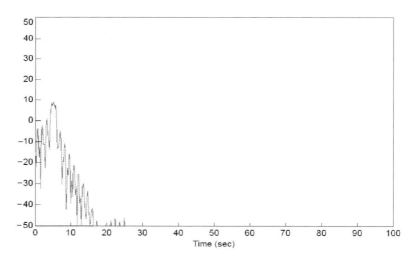

Figure 4.08: Spectrum of First Bandpass Filter Output

The spectrum of the bandpass filter output is limited to short frequencies (up to 12sec time mark) compared to the BPSK spectrum. Therefore, the bandpass filter has bandlimited the signal spectrum.

Figure 4.09 shows the up-converter carrier signal.

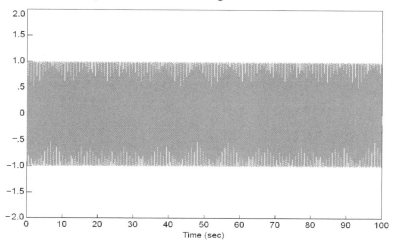

Figure 4.09: Up-Converter Carrier Centered at 6Hz

The sinusoid is not clearly visible as it is of high frequency. Figure 4.10 shows the frequency spectrum of this up-converter carrier signal.

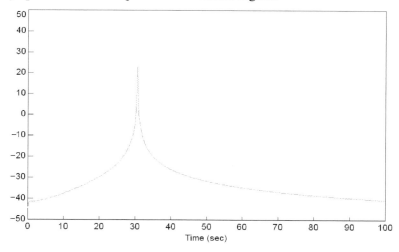

Figure 4.10: Spectrum of Up-Converter Carrier Signal

Roughly, it can be calibrated that the time position of the peak and the frequency as:

Frequency = time(sec)*0.2Hz.

For the 6Hz carrier, the peak occurs at 30 sec, which satisfies this relation.

Figure 4.11 shows the output of the up-conversion. Figure 4.12 shows the spectrum of the up-converted signal. The spectrum is now centered around the 6Hz up-converter carrier signal.

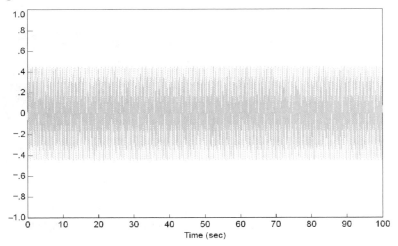

*Figure 4.11: Output After Up-conversion

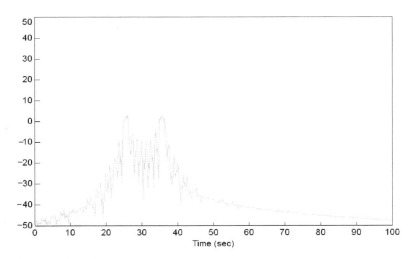

*Figure 4.12: Spectrum of Up-converted Output

Figure 4.13 shows the output of the bandpass filter that is placed after the up-conversion.

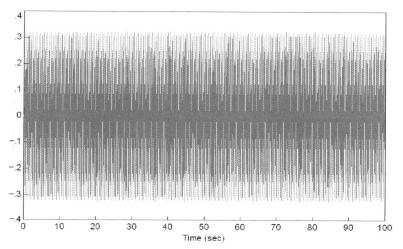

Figure 4.13: Bandpass Filter 2 Output

Figure 4.14 shows the spectrum of the bandpass filter output. The bandpass filter has transmitted signals only in the passband of the filter. This can be observed from the spectrum, which is not limited to a certain portion of the spectrum, rather than extending along the whole length of the bandwidth.

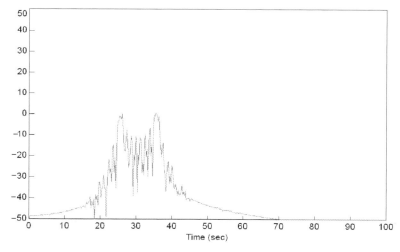

Figure 4.14: Spectrum of Bandpass Filter 2 Output

Figures 4.15 and 4.16 show the final output of the earth station transmitter after the low-noise amplifier. The spectrum of the signal is also shown in the immediate figure. The spectrum of the signal remained with in the same frequency band with an increase in the magnitude, caused due to the amplifier.

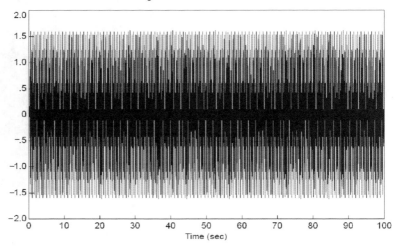

Figure 4.15: Earth Station Transmitter Final Output

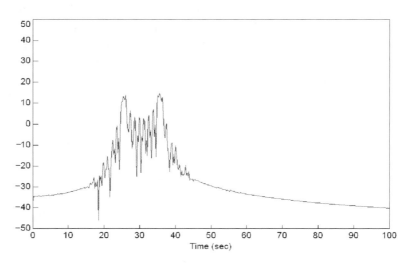

Figure 4.16: Spectrum of Earth Station Transmitter Final Output

Therefore, the baseband signal is first BPSK-modulated, bandpass-filtered twice, and up-converted to finally obtain this signal, which is centered around the uplink frequency of 6Hz (in reality it would be 6GHz).

Lab Activity Checklist

S. No.	Tasks	Completed	
		Yes	No
1.	Simulated the satellite earth station transmitter system in Commsim		
2.	Observed the signals and signal spectrums at different blocks of the system		

Lab Exercise 5—Satellite Transponder System

Objective

- Simulate the AWGN (Additive White Gaussian Noise) channel response in Commsim.
- Simulate the satellite transponder using Commsim.
- Study the working of the AWGN channel and the satellite transponder in Commsim.

Lab Setup

PC with Commsim simulator

Theory

The signal from the satellite earth station transmitter is sent along the LOS channel. This signal travels along the channel and is captured by the satellite transponder.

Figure 5.01 shows the earth station transponder, AWGN channel and the different blocks of the satellite transponder.

The AWGN channel adds white Gaussian noise to the signal. Also, since the travel distance is too high, an additional attenuation factor is included.

The satellite transponder takes the signals peak at 5Hz and 7Hz with centered at 6Hz and then multiplies it with the 2Hz signal. The bandpass filter transmits the signal centered at 4Hz frequency. This is then given to the high-power amplifier, the output of which is transmitted down to the earth station receiver. Therefore, the transponder acts as a satellite repeater with a frequency transformation from the frequency centered at 6Hz to frequency centered at 4Hz.

Problem Statement

Simulate and study the satellite transponder system.

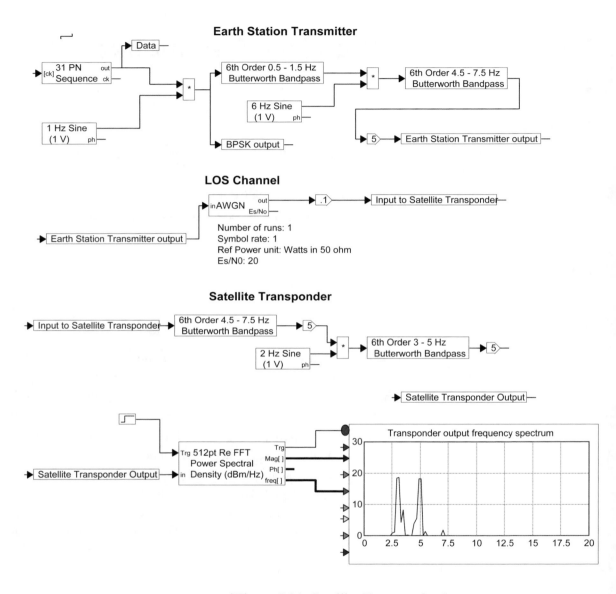

Earth Station Transmitter

*Figure 5.01: Satellite Transponder System

Procedure

1. Set up the circuit in Commsim as shown in Figure 5.01. The earth station transmitter is simulated in lab exercise 4 and is repeated here.

    To avoid crowded lines use variables (Blocks> Annotation> variable) in different units of the system and name them accordingly. In this way it is easy to study the signal trace in a different part of the system. For example to see the baseband data, connect the variable "Data" to the input of the plot.

2. To simulate the channel, use the AWGN channel block (Comm> Channels) and adjust its parameters as follows:

    > Number of runs: 1
    >
    > Symbol rate: 1
    >
    > Ref. Power unit: Watts in 50 ohm
    >
    > Es/N0: 20

3. Provide an attenuation block (Blocks> Arithmetic) to simulate the huge attenuation that takes place in satellite communications.

4. Give the output of the channel to the input of the bandpass filter of the transponder as shown in Figure 5.01, which is centered about 6Hz. Use a 6th order Butterworth filter (Comm> Filters> IIR). Set the lower frequency of the filter to 4.5Hz and the upper frequency to 7.5Hz.

5. Then the bandpass filter output is given to the amplifier (Blocks> Arithmetic), the output of which is frequency converted by multiplying with a carrier of 2Hz.

6. The resultant signal is connected to a bandpass filter to contain the downlink signal centered about 4Hz.

7. This signal is amplified before being transmitted down to the earth station receiver.

8. Connect the output of the gain block to Spectrum analyzer unit. Set the following for this unit:

    > Spectrum analyzer real: (Comm> Operators)
    >
    > > Trigger mode: Trigger
    > >
    > > Spectral Output: Mag/Phase
    > >
    > > FFT window type: Rectangular
    > >
    > > FFT size: 512
    > >
    > > Power Spectrum Unit: dBm/Hz
    > >
    > > Load: 50 ohms
    > >
    > > Output Frequency: Hz

9. Connect the Spectrum analyzer block to display. Use the following settings:

        External trigger: 0;

        XY Plot X=axis: 4

10. Use the following simulation properties (Simulate> Simulation Properties):

        Frequency: 100Hz

        End: 10

Run the simulation using the initial settings shown above, and record spectral information.

11. Use a display plot to study output of different blocks of the transmitter and trace the signal.

12. Check the frequency spectrum of different unit output and compare it with your analysis.

Conclusion/Observation

- The working of the AWGN channel and the satellite transponder system are analyzed.
- What can you infer about the spectrum of the AWGN noise added by the channel?
- Can you use any other filter as the bandpass filter other than the IIR filter?
- Why is the passband of the bandpass filter selected to be [4.5–7.5]Hz?

Solution Graphs

Figure 5.02 shows the noise added by the AWGN channel.

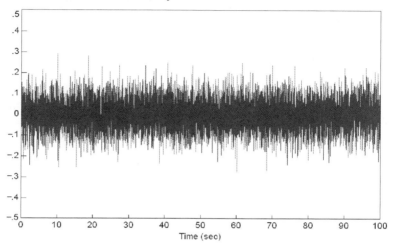

Figure 5.02: Noise Added by AWGN Channel

Figure 5.03 shows the input to the satellite transponder. It can be observed that the signal is greatly attenuated.

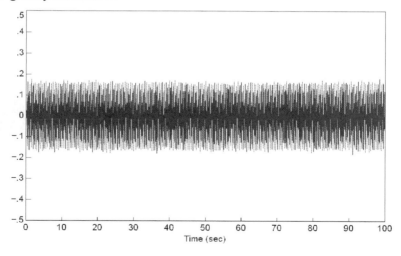

Figure 5.03: Satellite Transponder Input Signal

There are other spectral components that have come up due to the noise added. However, since the noise is AWGN, the spectrum of the added noise is also uniform over all the frequencies. Figure 5.04 shows the spectrum of the satellite transponder input signal.

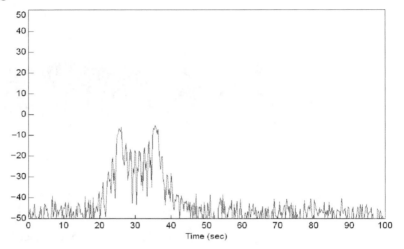

Figure 5.04: Satellite Transponder Input Signal Spectrum

Figure 5.05 shows the output of the bandpass filter of the satellite transponder.

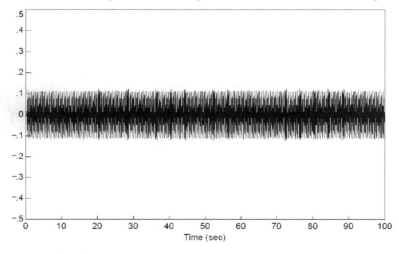

Figure 5.05: Bandpass Filter1 Output

The signal is band limited to the passband of the filter.

The spectrum of the signal is shown in Figure 5.06.

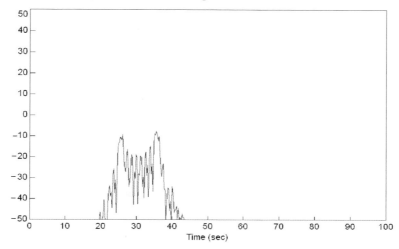

Figure 5.06: Spectrum of Bandpass Filter 1 Output

Figures 5.07 and 5.08 show the output of the amplifier that is present immediately after the bandpass filter of the transponder. The signal gets amplified. The magnitude of the signal spectrum is also increased.

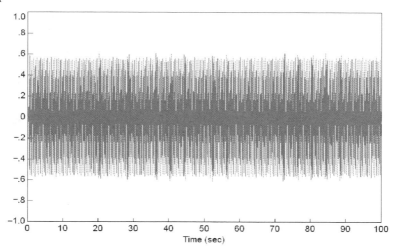

*Figure 5.07: Amplifier Output of Transponder

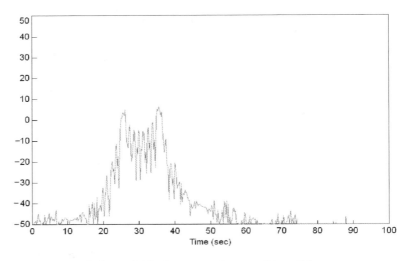

Time (sec)

*Figure 5.08: Spectrum Output of Amplifier

Figure 5.09 shows the carrier that is used in the transponder to make the frequency transformation. The carrier used is a sinusoid with central frequency of 2Hz. Figure 5.10 shows the spectrum of the transponder carrier signal.

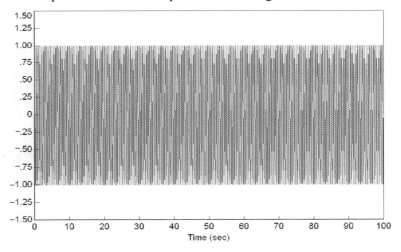

Time (sec)

Figure 5.09: Transponder Carrier Signal

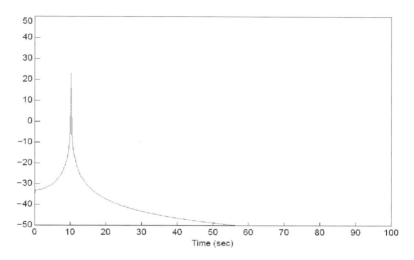

Figure 5.10: Transponder Carrier Signal Spectrum

Figure 5.11 shows output of the transponder frequency converter block. The corresponding spectrum is also shown in Figure 5.12.

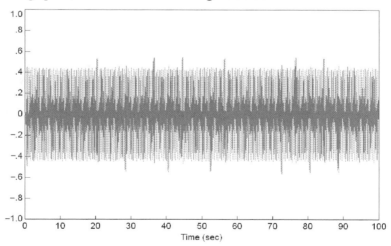

Figure 5.11: Transponder Mixing Output

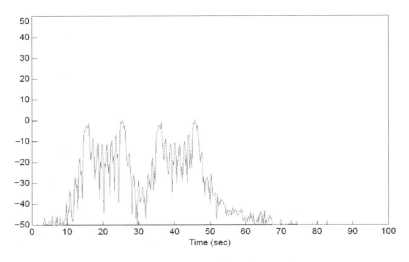

Figure 5.12: Transponder Mixing Output Spectrum

Figure 5.13 shows the output of the second bandpass filter of the satellite transponder.

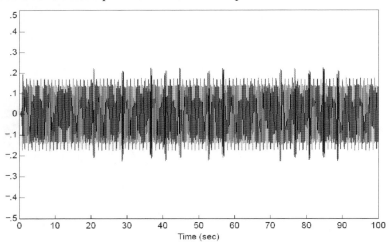

Figure 5.13: Bandpass Filter 2 Output

The signal is limited to the lower frequency spectrum region around the 4Hz carrier, which is the downlink frequency. The spectrum of the signal is shown in Figure 5.14.

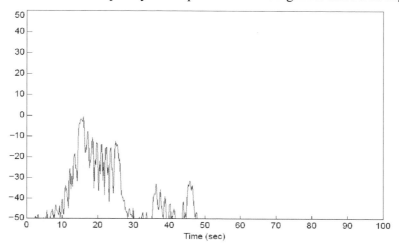

Figure 5.14: Spectrum of Bandpass Filter 2 Output

Figures 5.15 and 5.16 show the final output of the satellite transponder and its spectrum after the final amplifier.

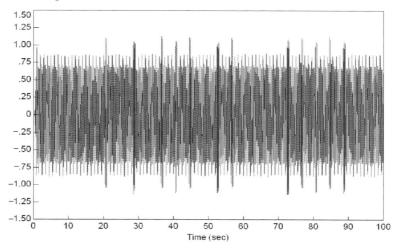

Figure 5.15: Transponder Final Output

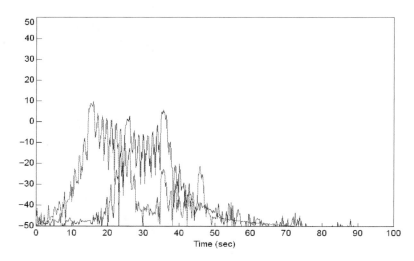

Figure 5.16: Spectrum of Final Transponder Output

Figure 5.17 shows the comparison of the spectral regions occupied by the transponder-received signal and the transmitted signal. The first region is the downlink frequency spectrum, and the second is the uplink frequency spectrum. They occupy different regions in the spectrum.

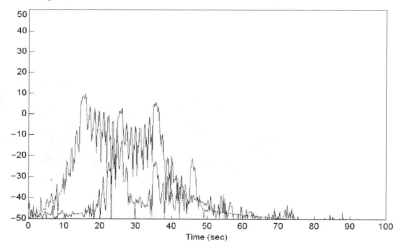

*Figure 5.17: Comparison of Transponder Input and Output Spectral Regions

To achieve better separation between the uplink and downlink spectral regions, the simulation is run for a different set of frequencies. Here the uplink frequency is centered around 12Hz and the downlink is centered around 8Hz.

Figure 5.18 shows the spectral separation for different sets of frequencies.

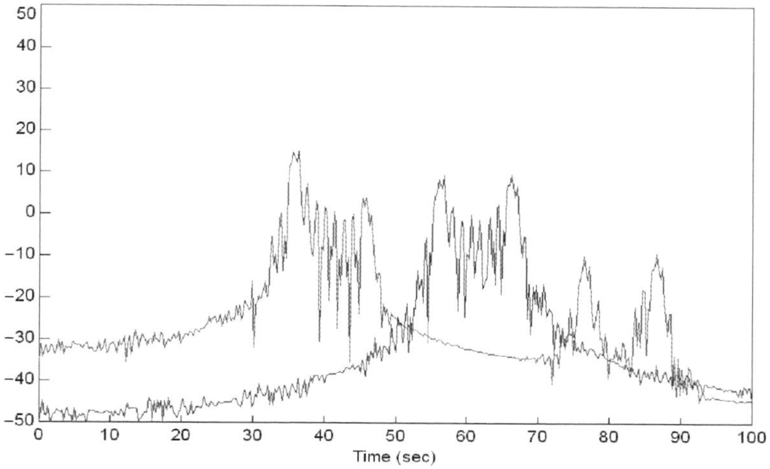

*Figure 5.18: Spectral Separation for Different Sets of Frequencies

Lab Activity Checklist

S. No.	Tasks	Completed	
		Yes	No
1.	Satellite transponder is simulated in Commsim		
2.	The signals at different blocks are observed and studied		

Lab Exercise 6—Satellite Earth Station Receiver System

Objective

Simulate the satellite earth station receiver system in Commsim.

Observe and analyze the signals at different blocks of the satellite earth station receiver system.

Lab Setup

PC with Commsim software

Theory

After the frequency translated signal is transmitted from the satellite transponder, the signal travels through the down link channel and is received at the earth station receiver.

Figure 6.01 shows the earth station transmitter, satellite transponder, satellite earth station receiver and up and down link channels.

The signal that is transmitted by the satellite transponder gets corrupted by AWGN and also attenuated by the time it reaches the earth station receiver. First the received signal is lowpass-filtered to remove the out-of-band frequency components added by the noise. Then the signal is amplified before subject to further processing. It is then down-converted using a carrier signal. The down-converted signal is lowpass-filtered to get the BPSK signal. This signal is BPSK-demodulated using the correlation receiver to finally recover the digital baseband information signal by using a decision circuit.

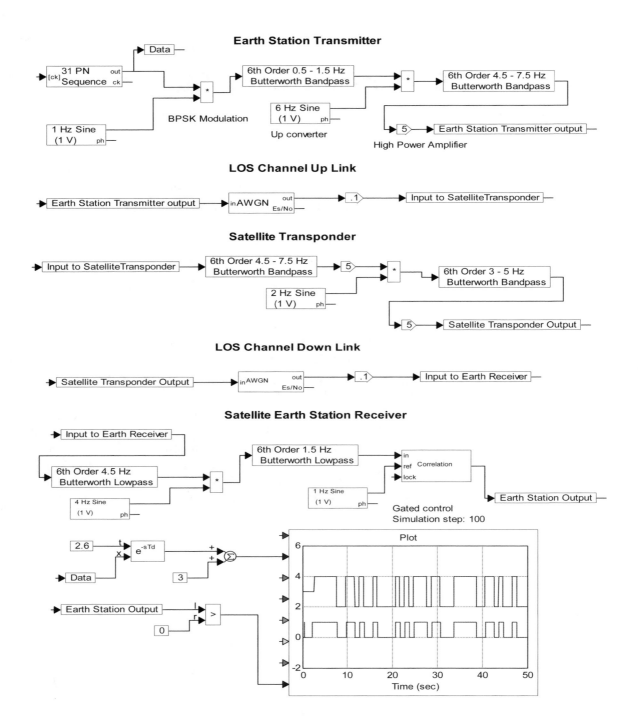

*Figure 6.01: Satellite Earth Station Receiver, Transmitter and Transponder

---

6.2 Satellite Earth Station Receiver System

Problem Statement

Simulate and study the satellite earth station receiver system.

Procedure

1. Set up the circuit as shown in Figure 6.01. Previous labs have discussed the earth station transmitter, up link channel, and satellite transponder. In this lab only the down link channel and satellite earth station receiver are added.

To avoid crowded lines use variables (Blocks> Annotation> Variable) in different units of the system and name them accordingly. In this way it is easy to study the trace of the signal in a different part of the system. For example to see the baseband data, connect the variable "Data" to the input of the plot.

2. To simulate the channel, use the AWGN channel block (Comm> Channels) and adjust its parameters as follows:

Number of runs: 1

Symbol rate: 1

Ref. Power unit: Watts in 50 ohm

Es/N0: 20

3. Provide an attenuation block (Blocks> Arithmetic) to simulate the huge attenuation that takes place in satellite communications.

4. Give the output of the down link channel to the input of the lowpass filter of the earth station receiver as shown in Figure 6.01 to remove out-of-band noise. Use a 6th order Butterworth filter (Comm> Filters> IIR). Set the cutoff frequency to about 4.5Hz.

5. Then the lowpass filter output is frequency down converted by multiplying with a carrier of 4Hz.

6. The resultant signal is connected to a lowpass filter to pass the signal lower than about 1.5Hz. The result is BPSK signal.

7. Use a 1Hz sinusoid (Comm> Signal sources) signal as the BPSK carrier.

8. Give the BPSK signal and the BPSK carrier to the correlator (Comm> Estimators> Correlation) receiver to recover the baseband digital information signal. Set the correlation parameters to gated control and simulation steps of 100.

9. Use the following simulation properties (Simulate> Simulation Properties):

Frequency: 100Hz

End: 50

10. Use a display plot to study output of different blocks of the transmitter and trace the signal.

11. Run the simulation and plot the graph of base band signal of earth station transmitter (Data) and compare it with the earth station receiver output. To set the time reference the same, the input signal is delayed by delay unit (Blocks> Delay) and also added a 3 unit to in order to be separated from the earth station output. In order to reconstruct the earth station digital output a decision circuit "greater than" (Blocks> Boolean) is used. This unit compares the output to zero. If the output is greater than zero generates one, otherwise generates zero.

12. Plot the signal at the output of different blocks and compare them with your analysis.

Conclusion/Observation

1. The signals at different blocks of the satellite earth station receiver system are observed and analyzed.
2. What is the effect of increasing the order of bandpass filter?
3. What is the effect of decreasing signal to noise ratio in AWGN unit?
4. Why is a low-pass filter used instead of a bandpass filter in the simulation?

Solution

Figure 6.02 shows the noise added by the AWGN channel as the signal traveled from the satellite transponder to the earth station receiver.

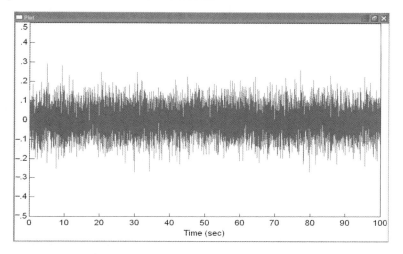

Figure 6.02: Noise Added by the Channel

Figure 6.03 shows the signal that is received at the earth station receiver after passing through the AWGN channel. The spectrum of the signal is also shown in Figure 6.04.

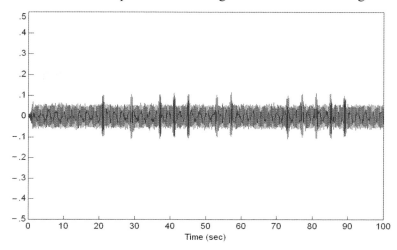

Figure 6.03: Spectrum of the Baseband Digital
Signal

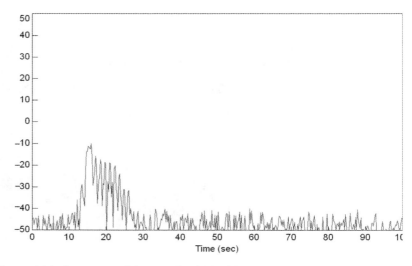

Figure 6.04: Spectrum of the Received Signal at the Earth Station Receiver

Figure 6.05 shows the output of the bandpass filter and its spectrum. The bandpass filter removed the out-of-band noise introduced by the AWGN channel.

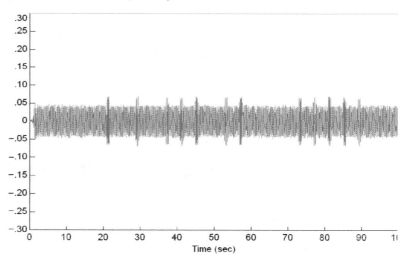

Figure 6.05: Bandpass Filter Output

The spectrum of output of the bandpass filter is shown in Figure 6.06.

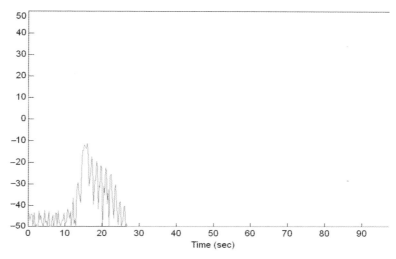

Figure 6.06: Spectrum of Bandpass Filter Output

Figure 6.07 shows the output of the amplifier. The signal is observed to be amplified. Also, the spectrum of the signal increases in magnitude. Here a low-pass filter is used because there is some noise in the lower end of the spectrum. Using a bandpass filter will remove even this noise.

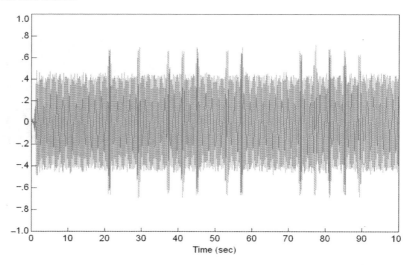

Figure 6.07: Output of Receiver Amplifier

The spectrum of the output of the amplifier is shown in Figure 6.08.

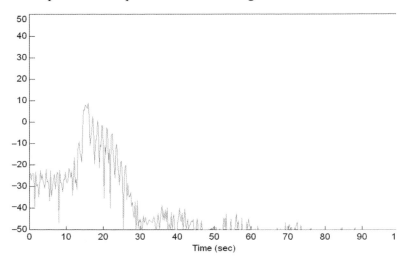

Figure 6.08: Spectrum of Receiver Amplifier Output

Figure 6.09 shows the carrier sinusoid that is used to down convert the signal. The carrier used is a 4Hz sinusoid.

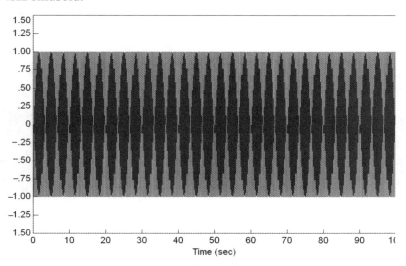

Figure 6.09: Receiver Down-converter Carrier Signal

Figure 6.10 shows the spectrum of receiver down-converter carrier signal.

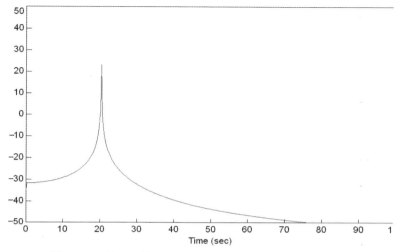

Figure 6.10: Receiver Down-converter Carrier Signal
Spectrum

Figure 6.11 shows the signal that is down-converted at the satellite receiver system. The result is the BPSK signal. However, the spectrum shows that it also contains a high frequency harmonic as a result of the multiplication.

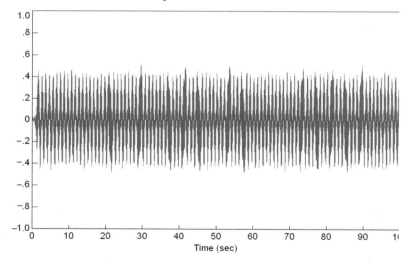

Figure 6.11: Down-Converted Signal

The spectrum of the signal is also shown in Figure 6.12.

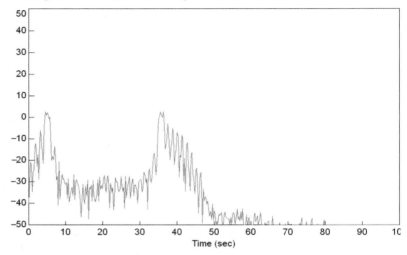

Figure 6.12: Spectrum of Down-Converted Signal

Figure 6.13 shows the output of the low-pass filter, which is used to remove the high frequency harmonics. The signal now contains only the BPSK signal.

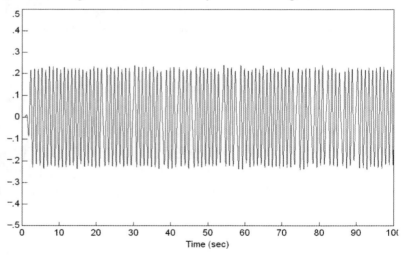

Figure 6.13: Output of Low-pass Filter

Figure 6.14 shows the spectrum of the output of the low-pass filter.

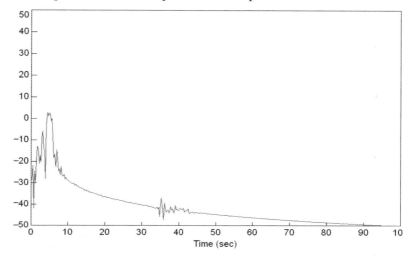

Figure 6.14: Spectrum of Output of Low-pass Filter

Figure 6.15 shows the BPSK carrier that is used as the reference signal to the correlator receiver.

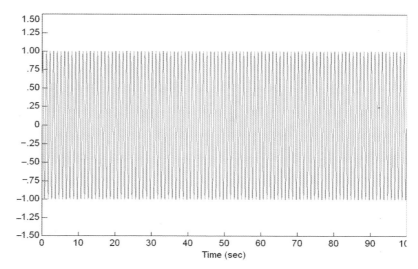

Figure 6.15: BPSK Carrier

The spectrum of the signal is also shown in Figure 6.16.

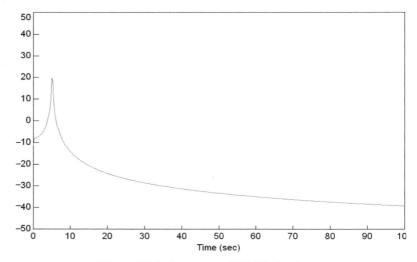

Figure 6.16: Spectrum of BPSK Carrier

The output of the correlator is shown in Figure 6.17.

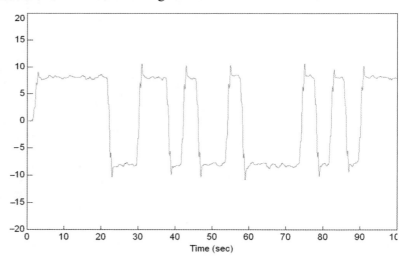

Figure 6.17: Correlator Output

The corresponding frequency of this output is also shown in Figure 6.18.

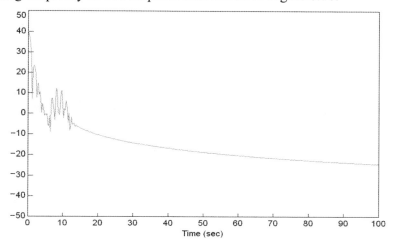

Figure 6.18: Corresponding Frequency of Correlator
Output

Figure 6.19 shows the comparison between the scaled correlator output and the original baseband digital information signal that is sent from the transmitter.

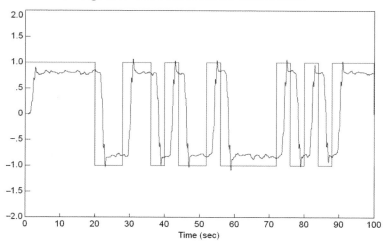

*Figure 6.19: Comparison Between Scaled Correlator Output and Original Baseband
Signal

The actual output signal that is recovered at the receiver would be the same as the input signal without any distortion, as the final output will not be the correlator output. But the final output will be the output of the decision circuit which will sample the output of the correlator at the decision instants and will produce a digital signal based on the output of the threshold detector. Therefore, the final output will be same as the original digital signal.

Lab Activity Checklist

S. No.	Tasks	Completed	
		Yes	No
1.	Simulated the satellite earth station receiver system in Commsim		
2.	Observed the signals and signal spectrums at different blocks of the system		

Lab Exercise 7—BPSK Signals Generation

Objective

Generate the BPSK signals that are to be multiplexed using an FDMA system.

Lab Setup

PC with Commsim software.

Theory

FDMA systems are used to generate BPSK signals. These signals can be generated by multiplying the NRZ bipolar digital sequence directly with the carrier.

Problem Statement

Generate three different BPSK signals from baseband NRZ codes.

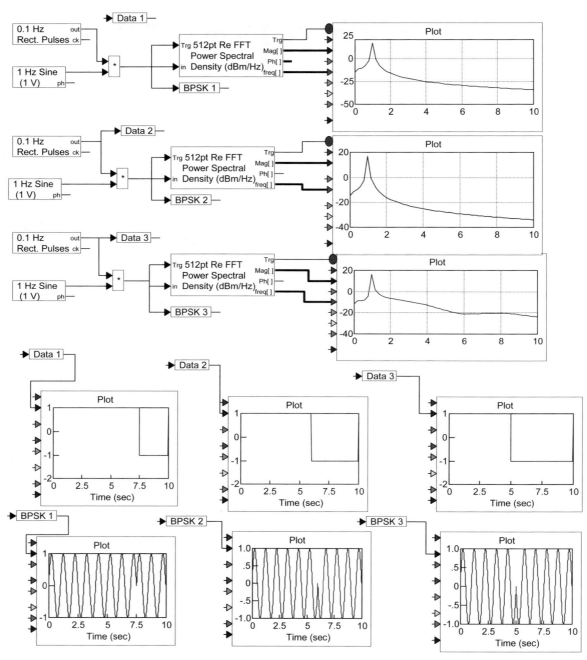

*Figure 7.01: BPSK Modulator

Procedure

1. Set up the circuit in Commsim as shown in Figure 7.01.

2. Give the carrier and the data signal to the multiplier (Blocks> Arithmetic) to generate the BPSK signal, as shown in Figure 7.01.

3. Use three 0.1Hz rectangular pulses (Comm> Signal sources) with different duty cycles as the NRZ digital data sources. Make sure that the high voltage is +1 and the low voltage is -1. Set the pulse mode to duty cycle. For example the percent of duty cycles could be 75, 60 and 50.

4. Use a sine wave (Comm> Signal sources) of 1Hz as the BPSK carrier.

5. Use the spectrum block (real) (Comm> Operators> Spectrum real) to obtain the spectrum of the BPSK signal. Set the following for this unit:

> Trigger mode: Continuous
>
> Spectral Output: Mag/Phase
>
> FFT window type: Rectangular
>
> FFT size: 512
>
> Power Spectrum Unit: dBm/Hz
>
> Load: 50 ohms
>
> Output Frequency unit: Hz

6. Connect the Spectrum analyzer block to display. Use the following setting for the display unit:

> Fixer Bound
>
> External trigger: 0;
>
> XY Plot X=axis: 4
>
> Y-Upper Bound: 20   X-Upper Bound: 10
>
> Y- Lower Bound: -50   X- Lower Bound: 0

7. Use the plot blocks to plot the different digital, carrier, and BPSK-modulated waveforms and their spectrums for the three modulators.

8. In order to avoid crowded wires use variable (Blocks> Annotation> Variable) and name them properly as shown in the Figure 7.01.

9. Simulate the circuit, and run the design. Use the following simulation properties (Simulate> Simulation Properties):

> Frequency: 100Hz
>
> End: 10

10. Plot and store the graphs. Measure the main frequency components of BPSK signal using spectrum analyzer and compare it with your analysis.

Conclusion/Observation

1. Three different BPSK-modulated waveforms are generated using Commsim.
2. What will be effect of increasing the number of FFT points in the spectrum analyzer?

Solution

Figures 7.02, 7.03, and 7.04 show the digital signal, carrier, and the first of the three BPSK signals generated for FDMA.

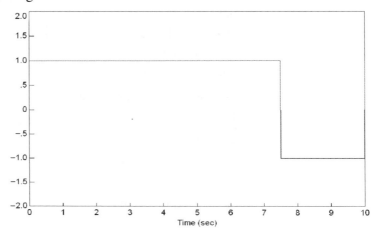

Figure 7.02: Digital Data Sequence 1 with 75 percent Duty Cycle and 0.1Hz Frequency

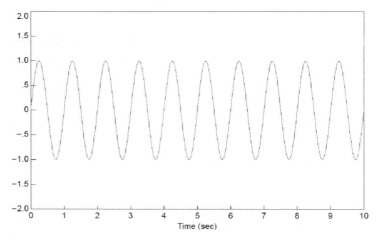

Figure 7.03: Carrier Signal, Sinusoid with 1Hz Frequency

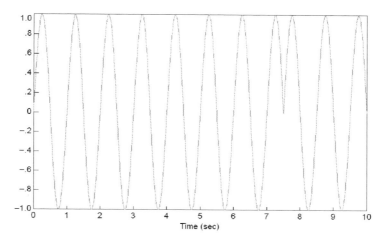

Figure 7.04: BPSK Output 1

Figures 7.05 and 7.06 show the second digital signal and the second BPSK output generated.

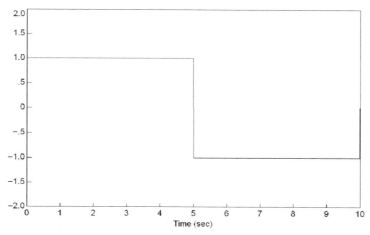

Figure 7.05: Digital Data Sequence 2 with 50 percent Duty Cycle and 0.1Hz Frequency

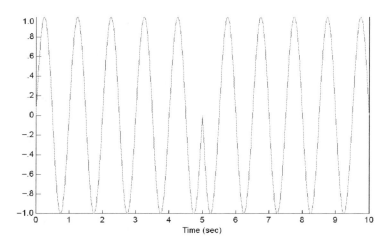

Figure 7.06: BPSK Output 2

Figures 7.07 and 7.08 show the third digital signal and the third BPSK output generated.

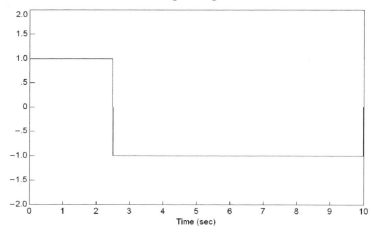

Figure 7.07: Digital Data Sequence 3 with 25 percent Duty Cycle and 0.1Hz Frequency

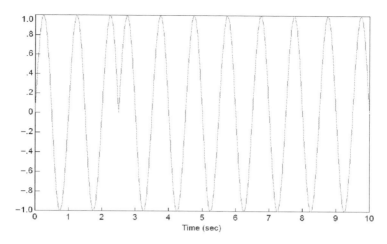

Figure 7.08: BPSK Output 3

Lab Activity Checklist

S. No.	Tasks	Completed	
		Yes	No
1.	Simulated BPSK modulator in Commsim		
2.	Generated three BPSK waveforms that can be given as input to the FDMA system		

Lab Exercise 8—BPSK Signals Multiple Access

Objective

Simulate and analyze the FDMA system using Commsim.

Lab Setup

PC with Commsim simulator

Theory

In an FDMA system, the different voice and data signals that occupy the same bandwidth in the frequency spectrum are converted to different frequency bands that do not interfere with each other. These signals are then mixed and sent along the channel. In effect, the available frequency is divided into different channels to which different baseband voice signals are accommodated.

Since different signals occupy different frequency bands, there is no interference and continuous data flow can exist between the transmitter and the receiver.

Problem Statement

Generate FDMA of the three BPSK signal.

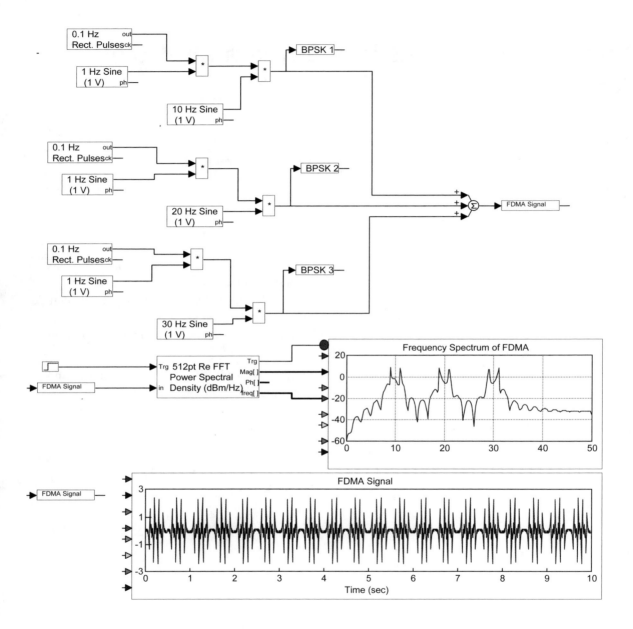

*Figure 8.01: FDMA System

8.2 BPSK Signals Multiple Access

Procedure

1. Setup the circuit in Commsim as shown in Figure 8.01.

2. The BPSK signal generation is the same as lab exercise 7 and repeated here. Give the carrier and signal to the multiplier (Block> Arithmetic) to generate the BPSK signal similar to previous lab exercise.

3. Use three sinusoidal (Comm> Signal Sources) carriers at frequencies 10Hz, 20Hz, and 30Hz to up-convert the different BPSK signals to different regions in the frequency spectrum.

4. Use multiplier block (Blocks> Arithmetic) to multiply the BPSK signals with the carriers for up-conversion.

5. Use the summing junction block (Block> Arithmetic) and add the three up-converted signals to obtain the FDMA signal. Add one input to the summing junction or use two summing junctions with two inputs each.

6. Use the spectrum block real (Comm> Operators> Spectrum real) to obtain the spectrum of the combined BPSK signals. Set the following for this unit:

    Trigger mode: Continuous

    Spectral Output: Mag/Phase

    FFT window type: Rectangular

    FFT size: 512

    Power Spectrum Unit: dBm/Hz

    Load: 50 ohms

    Output Frequency unit: Hz

7. Connect the Spectrum analyzer block to display. Use the following setting for the display unit:

    Fixer Bound

    External trigger: 0;

    XY Plot X=axis: 4

    Y-Upper Bound: 20   X-Upper Bound: 50

    Y-Lower Bound: -60   X- Lower Bound: 0

8. In order to avoid crowded wires use variable (Blocks> Annotation> Variable) and name them properly as shown in Figure 8.01.

9. Simulate the circuit, and run the design. Use the following simulation properties (Simulate> Simulation Properties):

Frequency: 100Hz

End: 10

10. Plot the spectrums of individual carriers, baseband signals, and up-converted signals.

11. Plot the spectrum of the FDMA signal. Measure the main frequency components of BPSK signals using spectrum analyzer and compare it with your analysis.

Conclusion/Observation

1. Working of the FDMA system is studied.

2. What will be the effect if the different up-converter frequencies are close to one another?

3. What will be the effect if the bandwidth of the BPSK signals is greater than the frequency separation between the up-converter frequencies?

Solution

Figures 8.02, 8.03, and 8.04 show the spectrums of the first BPSK signal, the 10Hz carrier, and the first of the three up-converted signals generated for FDMA, respectively.

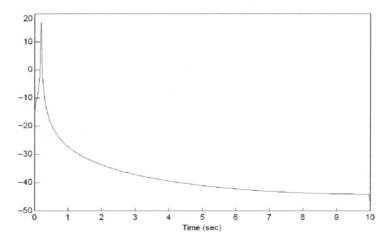

Figure 8.02: Spectrum of First BPSK Signal

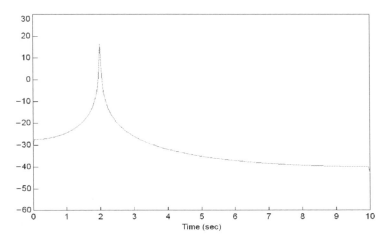

Figure 8.03: Spectrum of First Carrier Signal, 10Hz Channel

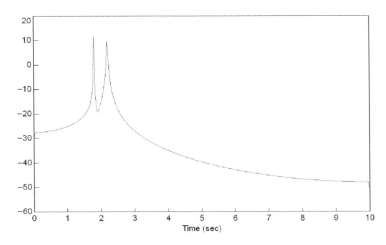

Figure 8.04: Spectrum of the First Up-Converted Signal, 10Hz Channel

Notice that the up-converted signal has two frequencies. These correspond to the upper and lower side-band frequencies. These will be located at f_c+f_b and f_c-f_b, where f_c is the frequency of the carrier (10Hz), and f_b is the frequency of the BPSK signal (1Hz).

Figures 8.05, 8.06, and 8.07 show the spectrums of the second BPSK signal, the 20Hz carrier, and the second of the three up-converted signals generated for FDMA.

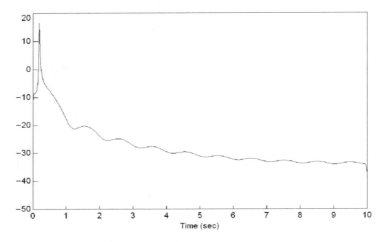

Figure 8.05: Spectrum of Second BPSK Signal

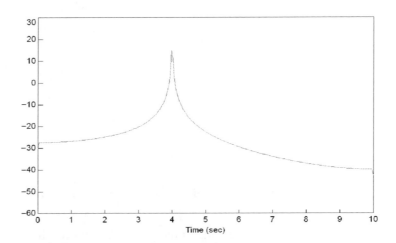

Figure 8.06: Spectrum of the Second Carrier Signal, 20Hz

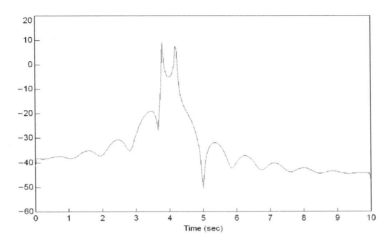

Figure 8.07: Spectrum of Second Up-Converted Signal, 20Hz Channel

You can see that the original spectrum of the BPSK signal is in the same frequency band and is then converted to a different location using the second carrier.

Figures 8.08, 8.09, and 8.10 show the spectrums of the third BPSK signal, the 30Hz carrier, and the third of the three up-converted signals generated for FDMA.

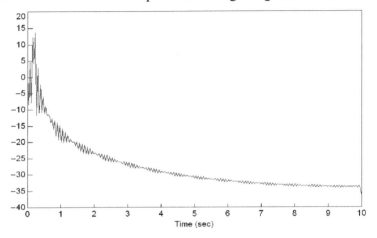

Figure 8.08: Spectrum of Third BPSK Signal

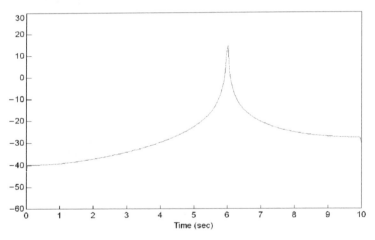

Figure 8.09: Spectrum of Third Carrier Signal, 30Hz

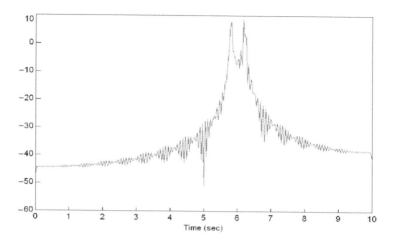

Figure 8.10: Spectrum of Third Up-Converted Signal, 30Hz Channel

You can see that the original spectrum of the BPSK signal is in the same frequency band and is then converted to a different location using the third carrier.

Figure 8.11 shows the final FDMA signal in time domain. This is the actual signal that will be transmitted over the channel instead of the three base-band signals.

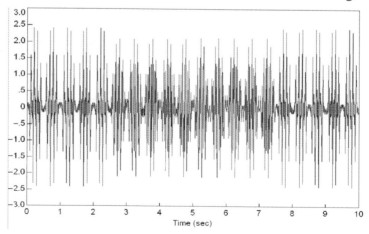

Figure 8.11: FDMA Signal

Figure 8.12 shows the spectrum of the combined FDMA signal. In this spectrum there are three different BPSK signals present in three different frequency regions.

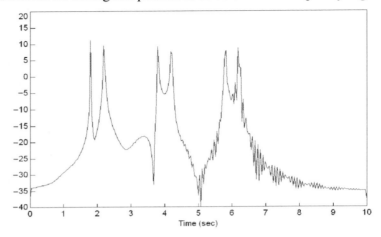

Figure 8.12: Spectrum of FDMA Signal

The shapes of the individual spectrums are preserved. There is no interference as the distance between the carriers in the spectrum is enough.

Lab Activity Checklist

S. No.	Tasks	Completed	
		Yes	No
1.	FDMA system is simulated in Commsim		
2.	FDMA system is studied and analyzed		

Lab Exercise 9—BPSK Signals Recovery

Objective

- Study, simulate, and analyze the FDMA receiver system using Commsim.
- Demodulate the BPSK signals and recover the original digital data signals.

Lab Setup

PC with Commsim simulator

Theory

The FDMA receiver system along with the transmitter and demodulation is shown in Figure 9.01. The received combined signal is given to each of the down-converting blocks that recover the base-band signals. First the combined signal is multiplied with each of the carrier signals. The output is then passed through a low pass filter. For BPSK demodulation, the output of the filter is given to the correlator, along with the BPSK carriers.

Problem Statement

To recover the individual BPSK signals and digital signals at the FDMA receiver system.

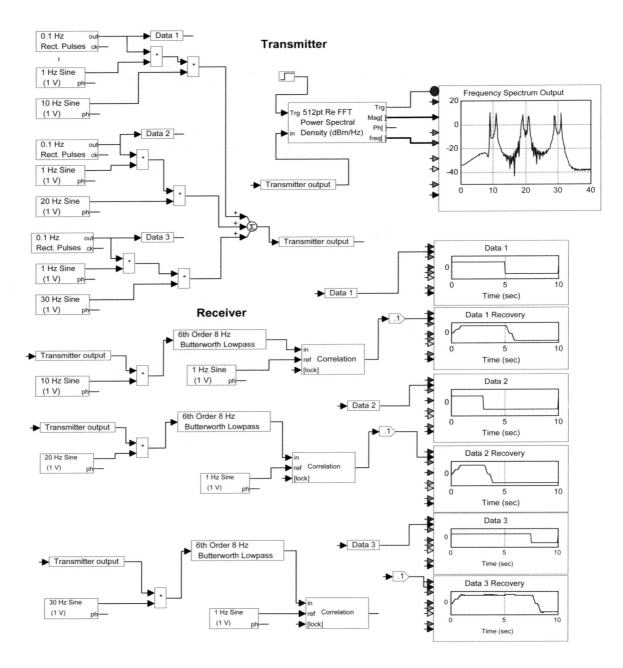

*Figure 9.01: FDMA Transmitter and the Receiver System with BPSK Modulation

Procedure

1. Set up the circuit in Commsim, as shown in Figure 9.01. Note that the figure also shows the FDMA transmitter system of lab exercise 8.

2. Use different carriers to down-convert the signals back to their 1Hz frequency by multiplying (Blocks> Arithmetic> Multiplier) it to the transmitter output. The carriers are 10Hz, 20Hz and 30Hz. as in the transmitter. Use variables (Blocks> Annotation> Variable) to connect the output of the transmitter to the different parts of the receiver system to avoid crowded figure.

3. Use 6th order low pass Butterworth filter (Comm> Filters> IIR). Set the cutoff frequency at 8Hz to filter the signals and recover only the base-band signal.

4. Give this recovered BPSK signal along with the BPSK carriers to the correlator (Comm> Estimators> Correlator) to demodulate and recover the digital signals. This block performs a correlation between two signals, herein referred to as the recovered signal and reference signal. Set the correlator to standard and window size to 100.

5. Reduce the gain by .1 in order to compare the demodulated output with the original signal. Use block Gain (Blocks> Arithmetic> Gain) and set it to .1.

6. Use different display units to show input data in the transmitter and the demodulated data in the output of the receiver.

7. Simulate the circuit, and run the design. Use the following simulation properties (Simulate> Simulation Properties):

    Frequency: 100Hz

    End: 10

8. Compare the input date to the transmitter with the recovered data in the receiver.

Study the spectrum of the signal in the output of multiplier, low pass filter and the correlator. Note the frequency components and compare it with your analysis. Use the same setting for spectrum unit as in lab exercise 8.

Conclusion/Observation

1. The FDMA receiver system and BPSK demodulation are studied.
2. What is the effect of multiplying the FDMA signal with any of the carrier signals?
3. Why is a low pass filter used immediately after multiplication with a carrier?
4. Can you think of any other method for recovering the individual BPSK signals from the composite FDMA signal?

Solution

Figures 9.02 and 9.03 show the resulting signal after the combined receiver signal is multiplied with the 10Hz carrier.

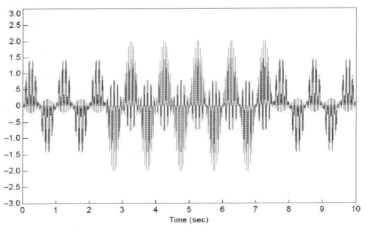

Figure 9.02: Signal After Multiplication with 10Hz Carrier

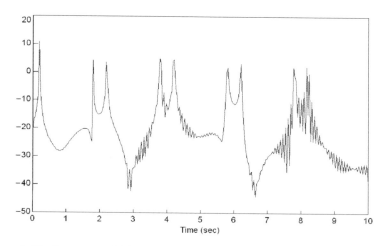

Figure 9.03: Spectrum of Signal After Multiplication with 10Hz Carrier

The combined signal has frequency components at 9, 11 (10Hz carrier), 19, 21 (20Hz carrier), and 29, 31 (30Hz carrier) frequencies. When this signal is multiplied, the following frequencies will result.

The 9 and 11Hz components will fall in the 1Hz region (the signal to be recovered).

The effect of the low pass filter is to recover exactly this signal. The output of the low pass filter is shown in Figures 9.04 and 9.05.

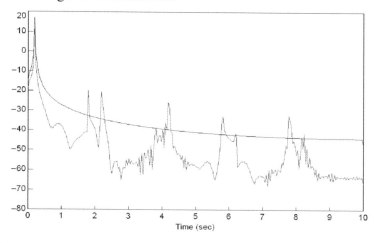

Figure 9.04: Spectrum of First Down-Converted Low Pass-Filtered Signal, 10Hz Channel, Compared to First BPSK Signal Spectrum

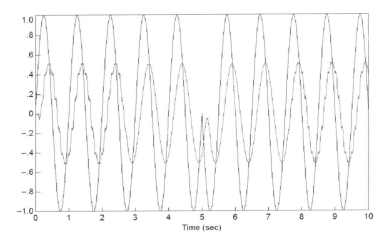

*Figure 9.05: Recovered First Down-Converted Low Pass-Filtered Signal, 10Hz Channel, Compared to Original First BPSK Signal

The frequency spectrum shows a perfect overlap of the frequencies. (Consider the peaks above 0; these are the main and strong components.) The comparison is better observed in the time domain where the exact signal with a little delay in time or phase is observed. The phase change of the BPSK signal is exactly recovered. Also, the recovered signal is a bit attenuated. Figure 9.06 shows the correlator output for the first signal.

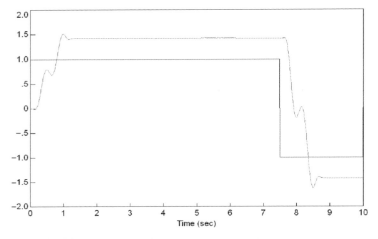

Figure 9.06: Correlator Output and First Digital Signal

The digital data is exactly recovered. The correlator output appears one second after the digital data, as the correlator output for the present symbol will be computed and sampled at the end of the symbol period. Figures 9.07 and 9.08 show the resulting signal after the combined receiver signal is multiplied with the 20Hz carrier.

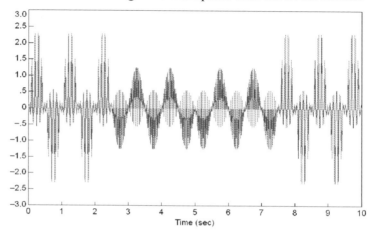

Figure 9.07: Signal After Multiplication with 20Hz Carrier

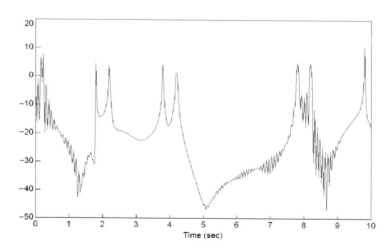

Figure 9.08: Spectrum of Signal After Multiplication with 20Hz Carrier

The 19 and 21Hz components will fall in the 1Hz region (the signal to be recovered) when multiplied with the 20Hz carrier. The effect of the low pass filter is to recover exactly this signal. The frequency spectrum and the output signal of the low pass filter is shown in Figures 9.09 and 9.10.

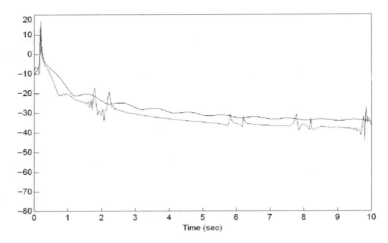

*Figure 9.09: Spectrum of Second Down-Converted Low Pass-Filtered Signal, 20Hz Channel, Compared with Second BPSK Signal Spectrum

The frequency spectrum in Figure 9.09 shows a perfect overlap of the frequencies. (Consider the peaks above 0; these are the main and strong components.)

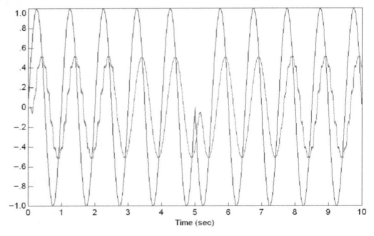

*Figure 9.10: Recovered Second Down-Converted Low Pass-Filtered Signal, 20Hz Channel in Comparison with the Original Second BPSK Signal (Blue = Original)

The comparison is better observed in the time domain where the exact signal with a little delay in time and phase is observed. The phase change of the BPSK signal is exactly recovered. Also, the recovered signal is a bit attenuated. Figure 9.11 shows the correlator output for the second signal. The digital data is exactly recovered.

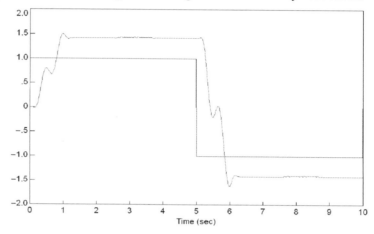

Figure 9.11: Second Correlator Output and Second Digital Signal

Figures 9.12 and 9.13 show the resulting signal after the combined receiver signal is multiplied with the 30Hz carrier.

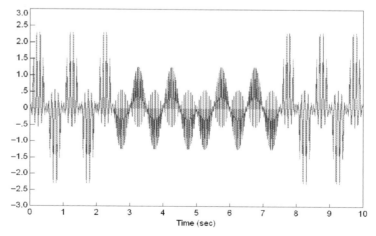

Figure 9.12: Signal After Multiplication with 30Hz Carrier

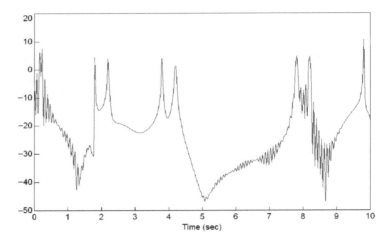

Figure 9.13: Spectrum of Signal After Multiplication with 30Hz Carrier

The 29 and 31Hz components will fall in the 1Hz region (the signal to be recovered) when multiplied with 30Hz signal. The effect of the low pass filter is to recover exactly this signal. The frequency spectrum and the output signal of the low pass filter is shown in Figures 9.14 and 9.15.

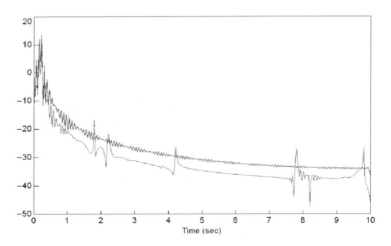

*Figure 9.14: Spectrum of Third Down-Converted Low Pass-Filtered Signal, 30Hz Channel, Compared with Third BPSK Signal Spectrum

The frequency spectrum, in Figure 9.15, shows a perfect overlap of the frequencies. (Consider the peaks above 0; these are the main and strong components.)

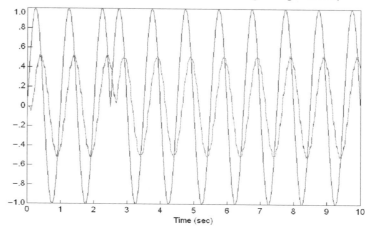

*Figure 9.15: Recovered Third Down-Converted Low Pass-Filtered Signal, 30Hz Channel, Compared with Original Third BPSK Signal

The comparison is better observed in the time domain where the exact signal with a little delay in time and phase is observed. The phase change of the BPSK signal is exactly recovered. Also the recovered signal is a bit attenuated. Figure 9.16 shows the correlator output for the third signal.

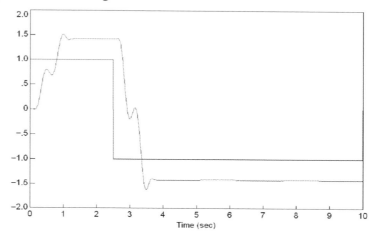

Figure 9.16: Third Correlator Output and Third Digital Signal

The digital data is exactly recovered.

Lab Activity Checklist

S. No.	Tasks	Completed	
		Yes	No
1.	FDMA receiver system was simulated in Commsim		
2.	All the multiplexed BPSK signals were recovered at the receiver		

Lab Exercise 10—QPSK Modulator

Objective

- Design the Quaternary PSK (QPSK) modulator in Commsim.
- Simulate, study, and observe the working of QPSK modulation in Commsim.

Lab Setup

PC with Commsim software.

Theory

QPSK modulation is an M-ary PSK modulation scheme. The number of bits symbol is $n = 2$, and so the bandwidth efficiency of this scheme is twice that of the BPSK modulation. As the number of bits per symbol is $n = 2$, the number of possible 2-bit combinations are $M = 2^n$ i.e. 4. Therefore, 4 different waveforms are required to represent these different bit combinations. However, since the QPSK signals can be generated from only 2 basis functions (sine and cosine), only 2 carrier signals are required. In fact a single carrier generator can be used, as the 2 basis function signals are quadrature components that can be derived from the same carrier with a suitable phase shift.

The block diagram of the QPSK modulator is shown in Figure 10.01.

The I-channel and Q-channel bits are obtained from the serial-to-parallel converter. The I-channel is modulated by the cosine signal and the Q-channel by the sine signal. The final QPSK signal is the summation of these two signals.

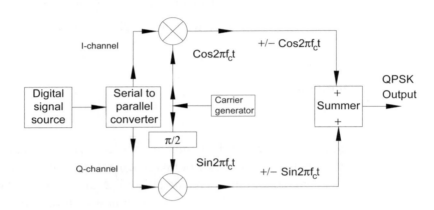

Figure 10.01: QPSK Modulator

Problem Statement

Design and simulate QPSK modulator in Commsim and observe the signals at different intermediate blocks.

The block diagram shown in Figure 10.01 describes the components required. It is better to search through the various blocks available in Commsim and come up with your own design schematic.

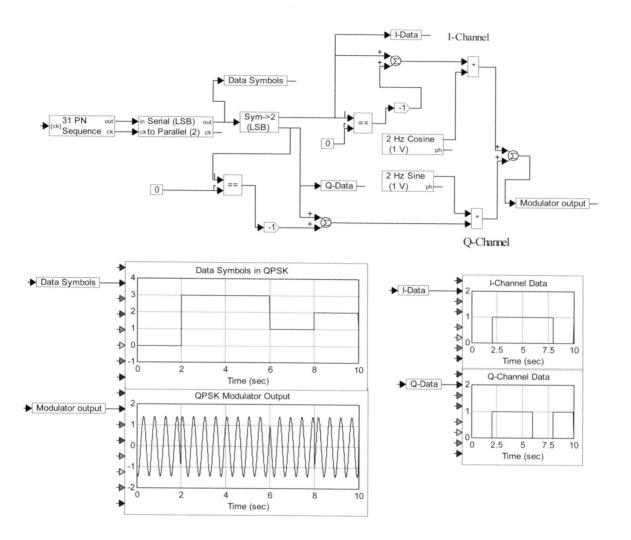

*Figure 10.02: QPSK Modulator

Procedure

1. The Commsim simulation schematic of the QPSK is shown in Figure 10.02.

Use a PN code generator (Comm>Signal sources) as the digital data source. (You may even use simple rectangular pulses, but you have to play around a little bit more to get the different bit combinations in the symbol periods.) Set the following parameters for this unit:

Shift register size: 5   Output Mode: Bilevel (-1,+1)

Timing: Internal   Bit rate (bps): 1

Use default for the rest of the parameters.

2. Use serial to parallel (Comm>Digital) unit to convert the binary data in to four different levels. Use 2-bits per symbol and LSB first for bit order. The serial to parallel converter did not output 2 parallel bits for every 2 serial bits, but gave the decimal value of the 2 bits as the output.

3. Connect the output of serial to parallel converter to Symbol to bits (Comm>Digital)

unit. Use LSB first and the number of output bits to two. This block takes the symbol as input and then outputs the individual bits. One of the two bits is taken as the I-channel bit, and the other is taken as the Q-channel bit.

It should be noted that the bit pattern that is output from the symbol to bits block is

the NRZ unipolar code (0, 1), whereas it is required to have NRZ bipolar code (−1, +1) for the modulation purpose.

The blocks used for this conversion are "equal to" block (Blocks>Boolean), gain (Blocks>Arithmetic) and a constant block (Blocks>Signal producer). Use a summing junction (Block>Arithmetic) to perform the final stage of this operation.

This part of the design converts zero data to -1 level and no change if the data is +1 level.

5. Use multipliers (Blocks>Arithmetic) to multiply the data in I and Q channel by 2Hz sinusoid signals (Comm>Signal sources) as the carrier.

6. Add the outputs of I and Q-channel using a summing junction (Blocks>Arithmetic).

7. Simulate the circuit, and run the design. Use the following simulation properties (Simulate> Simulation properties):

> Frequency: 100 Hz
>
> End: 10

Run the simulation for enough time so that you can observe the different bit combinations being represented by the different waveforms.

8. Plot the graphs at the output of each block and analyze them. In order to avoid crowded figures use variable (Blocks>Annotation) with proper names to connect different part of the system to display unit.

9. Based on the PN code output, theoretically determine the I-channel bits and the Q-channel bits.

10. Explain how the I and Q channel data are converted to bilevel.

11. Compare the theoretically obtained plots with the simulation plots.

Conclusion/Observation

▨ The working of the QPSK modulation is simulated in Commsim.

▨ What determines the I-channel and Q-channel bits in the simulation?

▨ Does the output of the serial-to-parallel converter have the required NRZ bipolar bits?

▨ Think of some circuits that can change the NRZ unipolar bits to NRZ bipolar bits.

Solution

The different outputs of the different blocks of the simulation schematic are shown in the following figures.

The digital signal as generated by the PN code generator is shown in Figure 10.03.

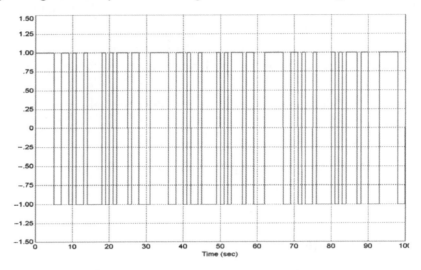

Figure 10.03: Digital Data Signal

The clock of this digital signal is shown in Figure 10.04.

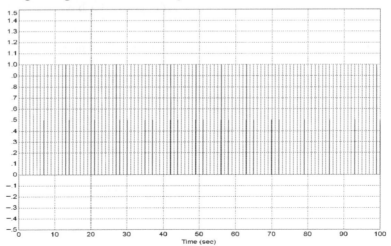

Figure 10.04: Digital Signal Clock Signal

The bit rate of the PN code generator is 1 bps. Also, it can be seen that the digital signal is NRZ bipolar.

Figure 10.05(a) shows the output of the serial-to-parallel converter.

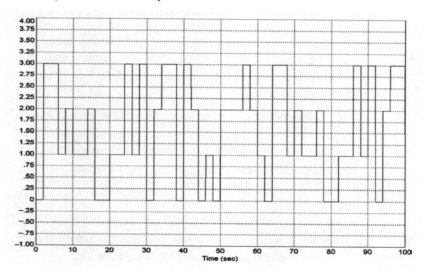

Figure 10.05(a): Serial-to-Parallel Converter Block Output

The output clock of the signal is also shown in Figure 10.05(b).

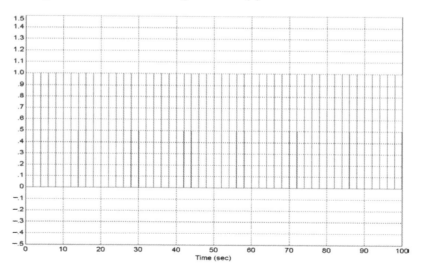

Figure 10.05(b): Serial-to-Parallel Converter Block Clock Signal

The serial-to-parallel block clock signal is double-space wide on the time axis compared to the original digital signal. Therefore, the data rate of the signal is reduced by half. The output of the serial-to-parallel converter is similar to a level generator.

The serial parallel converter did not output 2 parallel bits for every 2 serial bits, but gave the decimal value of the 2 bits as the output. It acts similar to a level generator.

So the output of the serial-to-parallel converter is not 2 parallel bits, but the symbol. So it takes in individual bits and outputs the symbol level spread across the symbol period (the symbol period is equal to the sum of the time period of the total bits that go with 1 symbol).

Watch out which of the 2 bits is taken out first (LSB or MSB). You need to use the same specification when you use the parallel-to-serial converter at the receiver end when performing demodulation.

Figure 10.06 shows the output of the symbol to bits block. This block takes the symbol as input and then outputs the individual bits. One of the two bits is taken as the I-channel bit, and the other is taken as the Q-channel bit.

Once again, watch out which of the 2 bits is taken out first (LSB or MSB). You need to use the same specification when you use the bits to symbol converter at the receiver end when performing demodulation.

Figure 10.06(a) shows the I-channel bits.

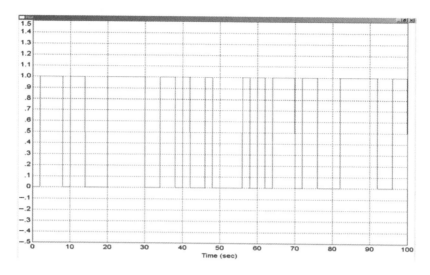

Figure 10.06(a): I-Channel Bits

Figure 10.06(b) shows the Q-channel bits.

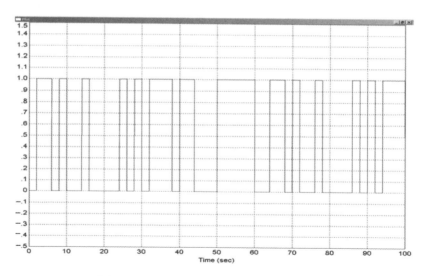

Figure 10.06(b): Q-Channel Bits

It can be observed that the actual digital bit pattern is split between the I-channel and the Q-channel. However, it should be noted that the bit pattern that is output from the symbol to bits block is the NRZ unipolar code (0, 1), whereas it is required to have NRZ bipolar code $(-1, +1)$ for the modulation purpose.

Figure 10.07 shows the I-channel carrier signal.

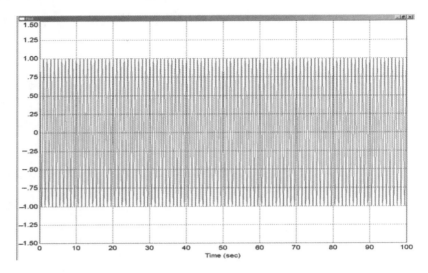

Figure 10.07: I-Channel Carrier Signal

Figure 10.08 shows the NRZ bipolar code of the I-channel. A simple logic is used to generate the NRZ unipolar code into NRZ bipolar code. This can be accomplished in any manner.

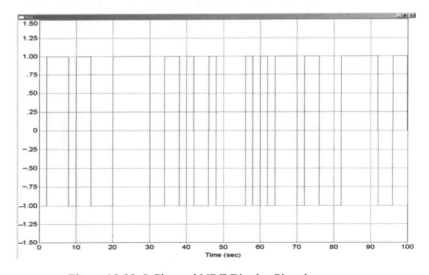

Figure 10.08: I-Channel NRZ Bipolar Signal

Figure 10.09 shows the final modulated I-channel signal.

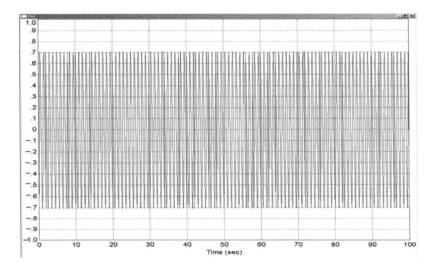

Figure 10.09: I-Channel Signal

Figure 10.10 shows the Q-channel carrier signal. This is in quadrature to the carrier signal that is used in the I-channel.

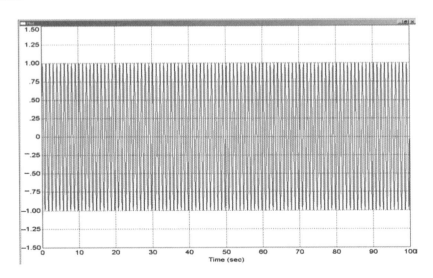

Figure 10.10: Q-Channel Carrier Signal

Figure 10.11 shows the Q-channel NRZ bipolar code (obtained by converting the NRZ unipolar code output from the symbol to bits block).

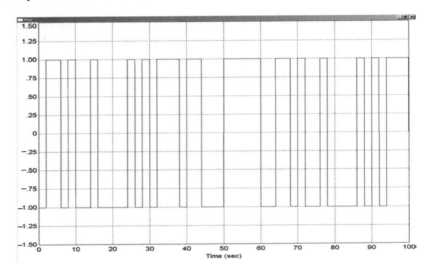

Figure 10.11: Q-Channel NRZ Bipolar Bit Pattern

Figure 10.12 shows the final Q-channel modulated signal (modulated by this quadrature carrier signal).

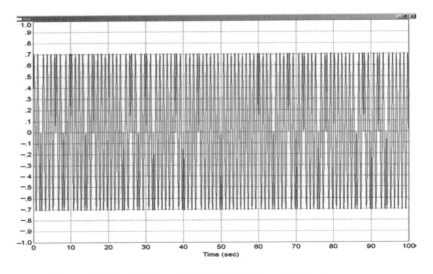

Figure 10.12: Q-Channel Modulated Signal Output

Figure 10.13 shows the final QPSK signal output. This is obtained by summing up the I-channel signal and the Q-channel signal.

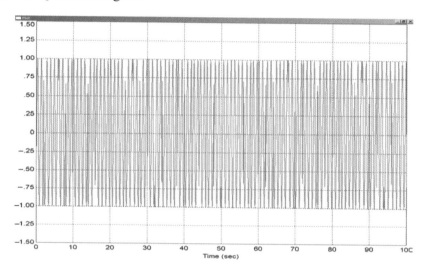

Figure 10.13: QPSK Modulated Output

Lab Activity Checklist

S. No.	Tasks	Completed	
		Yes	No
1.	The QPSK modulator is simulated in Commsim		
2.	The signals at the output of the different blocks of the QPSK modulator are observed		
3.	The working of the QPSK modulator is studied in Commsim		

Lab Exercise 11—QPSK Demodulation

Objective

- Simulate the QPSK demodulator in Commsim.
- Observe the different signals at the output of the different blocks of the QPSK demodulator.
- Study the working of the QPSK demodulation.

Lab Setup

PC with Commsim software.

Theory

QPSK demodulation, once again, can be done using only 2 correlators as there are only 2 basis functions used in the modulation.

Figure 11.01 shows the QPSK demodulator block diagram.

The working of the QPSK demodulator is similar to any other digital demodulation. The received signal is multiplied with the cosine carrier signal to recover the I-channel signal. Similarly, the same received signal is multiplied with the sinusoid quadrature carrier signal to recover the Q-channel component. Then the product signals are sent to the integrator and dump circuit. The multiplication and integration together will complete the correlation process.

The output of the integrate and dump circuits will recover the I-channel and Q-channel bits. The 2-bit patterns are given to the parallel-to-serial converter, which finally gives the recovered digital signal.

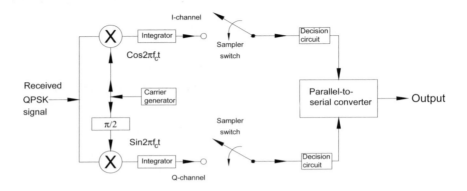

Figure 11.01: QPSK Demodulator Block Diagram

Problem Statement

Simulate, study, and observe the working of the QPSK demodulation in Commsim.

It is better not to provide the simulation schematic directly to the students. The block diagram shown in Figure 11.01 describes the components required. It is better to let the students search through the various blocks available in Commsim and come up with their own design schematic.

The schematic for the QPSK demodulation is shown in Figure 11.02.

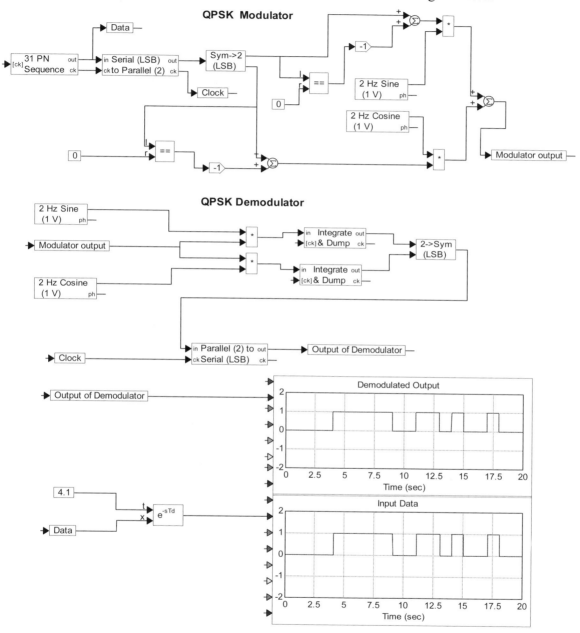

*Figure 11.02: QPSK Modulation and Demodulation System

Procedure

1. The Commsim schematic for the QPSK modulator and demodulation is shown in Figure 11.02. Note that the figure also shows the QPSK modulator of lab exercise 10.

   Using a variable block (Blocks>Annotation) give the output of the QPSK modulator circuit from the previous lab exercise as the input to the QPSK demodulator.

2. Use the same modulator carrier signals in the demodulator.

3. Connect the outputs of the two multiplier to the input of integrate and dump block (Comm>Operators>Integrate and Dump (real)). This block implements an "integrate and dump" operation on the input signal. The input signal is continuously integrated and the integral output is periodically "dumped" and reset to a specified value. The dump rate can be specified internally, or through an external clock. When this block is used to demodulate a baseband phase modulated signal, it should be followed by the appropriate detector block for the modulation used. Use the following settings for this unit:

Reset value: 0	Scale Factor: 1
Dump timing: Internal	Output mode: Held
Dump Rate (Hz): 0.5	Integration Method: Euler

4. Using Bit to symbol unit (Comm>Digital) to convert the individual bits from the two channels to form the decimal equivalent values. Set the LSB first and number of input bits to two.

5. Connect the output of the bits to symbol block to the input of parallel to serial block (Comm>Digital). This block accepts parallel data represented by symbol numbers and outputs a serial binary stream. The output bits are obtained by decomposing the binary representation of the input symbol number. For this block set the LSB first, number of inputs to two and output bit rate to one.

6. Simulate the circuit, and run the design. Use the following simulation properties (Simulate> Simulation properties):

   Frequency: 100Hz

   End: 20

7. Plot the graphs of the outputs of each of the blocks in the demodulator and analyze it.

8. Plot the data signal and the recovered digital signal after demodulation on the same graph and analyze it. See the following note.

While plotting them on the same graph, care should be taken to give appropriate delay to the original digital signal, as there would be some time delay with which the output is produced. Use the Delay unit (Block>Time delay) and give enough delay time to see input data and the demodulated output in the same time scale.

Conclusion/Observation

- A QPSK demodulator is simulated in Commsim, and its workings are studied.
- Is the recovered signal exactly the same as the original digital signal?
- What could be reason for the delay encountered in the reproduction of the digital signal at the demodulator?
- Is the output of the parallel-to-serial converter NRZ bipolar or NRZ unipolar?

Solution

Figure 11.03 shows the I-channel carrier signal that is multiplied with the received signal.

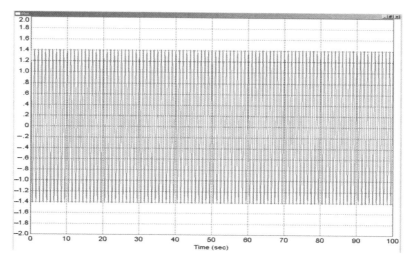

Figure 11.03: I-Channel Carrier Signal

Figure 11.04 shows the I-channel product signal obtained by multiplying the received signal with the I-channel cosine carrier signal.

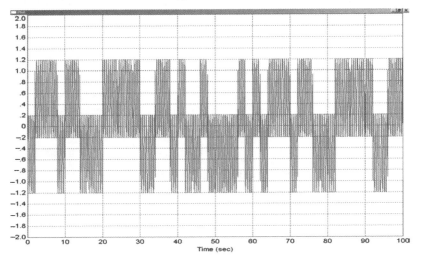

Figure 11.04: I-Channel Product Signal

Figure 11.05 shows the output of the integrator and dump circuit for the product signal as input.

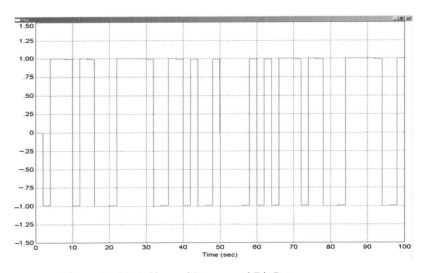

Figure 11.05: I-Channel Recovered Bit Pattern

Figure 11.06 shows the Q-channel carrier signal that is multiplied with the received signal.

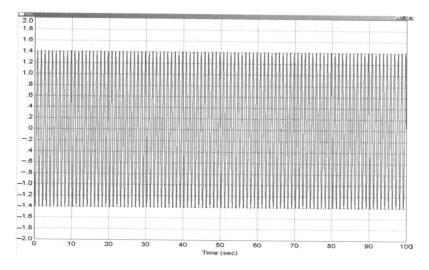

Figure 11.06: Q-Channel Carrier Signal

Figure 11.07 shows the Q-channel product signal obtained by multiplying the received signal with the Q-channel sine carrier signal.

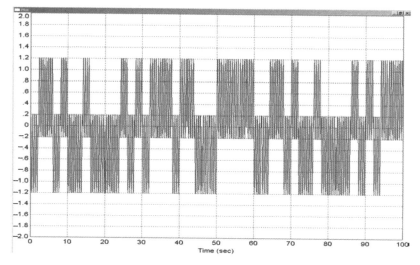

Figure 11.07: Q-Channel Product Signal

Figure 11.08 shows the integrator output for the Q-channel.

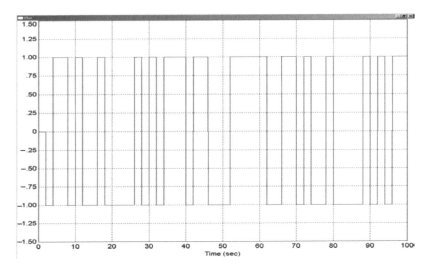

Figure 11.08: Q-Channel Integrate and Dump Circuit Output

Figure 11.09 shows the output of the bits2symbol block. The individual bits from the two channels are used to form the decimal equivalent values.

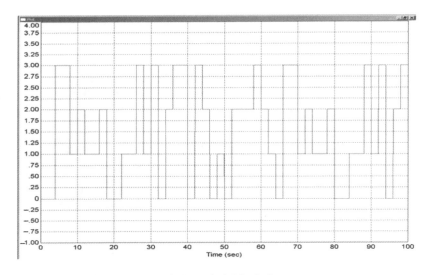

Figure 11.09: Bits2symbol Block Output

Figure 11.10 shows the NRZ unipolar data, which is given by the parallel-to-serial converter block.

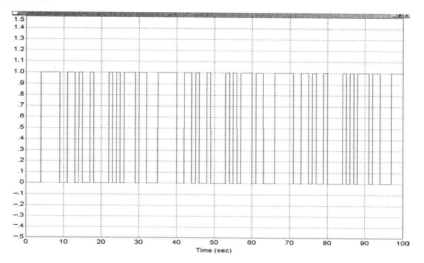

Figure 11.10: NRZ Unipolar Output

Figure 11.11 shows the NRZ bipolar signal that is generated from the NRZ unipolar data.

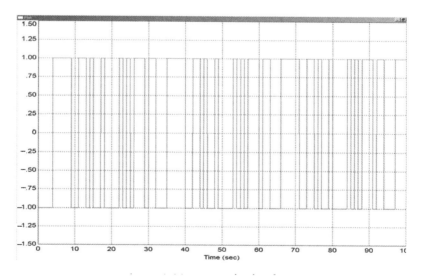

Figure 11.11: NRZ Bipolar Output

Figure 11.12 shows the comparison between the original digital signal that is modulated at the modulator and the final recovered digital signal at the demodulator. To observe them, the original digital signal is given suitable attenuation and time delay.

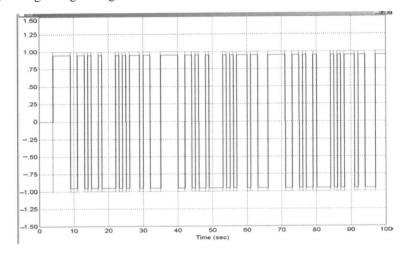

*Figure 11.12: Comparison of Original Digital Signal and Signal Recovered at Demodulator

Lab Activity Checklist

S. No.	Tasks	Completed	
		Yes	No
1.	QPSK demodulator is simulated in Commsim		
2.	Various signals at different blocks are observed and the workings of the QPSK demodulator are studied		
3.	Sync is achieved between modulator and demodulator		

Lab Exercise 12—QAM Modulator Design with Different Constellations

Objective

- Design the Quadrature Amplitude Modulation (QAM) modulator in Commsim.
- Simulate, study, and observe the working of QAM in Commsim.
- Design the QAM with a (1, 7) 8-QAM constellation, and study its operation.
- Design the QAM with a (4, 4) 8-QAM star constellation, and study its operation.
- Design the 8-QAM with the triangular constellation, and study its operation.
- Design the 8-QAM with square constellation, and study its operation.

Lab Setup

PC with Commsim software.

Theory

QAM is an M-ary technique in which both the amplitude and phase of the modulated signal are varied. It is also known as amplitude shift keying. In this lab exercise, you will study the operation of an 8-QAM modulation for different constellations. There are eight reference signals that are transmitted for different combinations of $n = \log_2 M = 3$-bit combinations.

The Commsim block diagram of the QAM modulator is shown in Figure 12.01.

Since only two basis functions are required to generate the QAM signal, only two carriers (quadrature components of the same carrier) are used. The original digital signal is given to the serial to parallel converter (Comm>Digital). This block accepts a serial binary stream and outputs parallel data as symbol numbers. The bits can be provided either LSB first or MSB first. The symbol value is obtained by combining sets of n input bits at a time, where n is equal to 3 here. The output of this unit is shown in Figure 12.01. Considering three bits in serial input combination, this unit converts them to eight different voltage levels (0 V to 7 V).

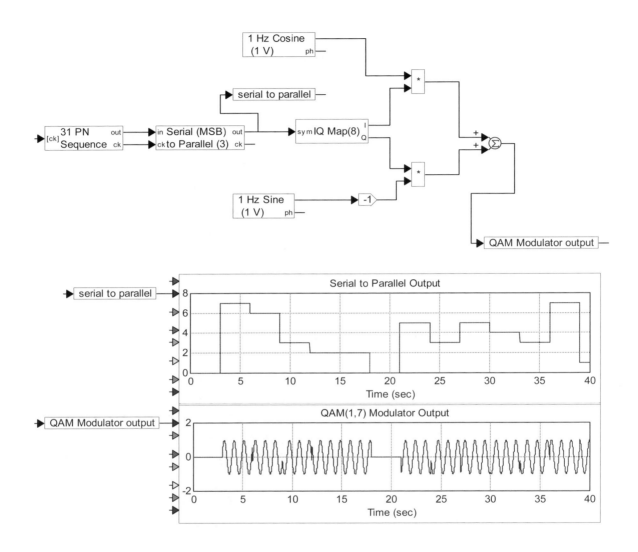

*Figure 12.01: QAM Modulation

The output of serial to parallel unit is connected to IQ Mapper (Comm>Operators>IQ Mapper). This block allows the user to specify an arbitrary IQ constellation via an external file. The block accepts a symbol value in the range of [0, 1, 2, N-1] and outputs a pair of I and Q values as specified by the mapping file. This block can be followed by the IQ Modulator block to achieve modulation of arbitrary user defined constellations. The settings of this unit are as follows:

a) Constellation Size

Specifies the size N of the constellation used by the IQ Mapper block.

b) Select File

Opens the Select File dialog box for selecting the IQ Mapper constellation file.

c) Browse File

Opens the selected IQ Mapper constellation file using Notepad.

d) File Path

Specifies the DOS path to the desired IQ Mapper constellation file. The format of the mapping file is described below:

File header

Symbol number	I output	Q output
...		

The symbol number values need not be entered in increasing order, although it is highly recommended to do so for clarity. The table must contain a total of N entries, where N is the constellation size.

Table entries may be separated by blank spaces, tabs, or commas. Blank lines are also acceptable. The file should be generated in Notepad. An example of an IQ map file for QAM (1, 7) is shown below:

QAM (1, 7) Map File: Not Grey Encoded

0	0	0
1	1	0
2	0.62348980185873	0.78183148246803
3	-0.22252093395631	0.97492791218182
4	-0.90096886790242	0.43388373911756
5	-0.90096886790242	-0.43388373911756
6	-0.22252093395631	-0.97492791218182
7	0.62348980185873	-0.78183148246803

This file should be saved as QAM (1, 7).dat in the following file path:

C:\Commsim\Commlib\QAM (1, 7).dat

The first line is the file header. The first column is the symbol number. The second column is the generated amplitude for the I-Channel and the third column is the generated amplitude for the Q-channel. In the I and Q Channels these amplitude (voltage) are then multiplied by the carrier signals, and the two channel signals are added up to obtain the final QAM signal. Use the summing junction block (Blocks>Arithmetic) for this addition. The modulator circuit diagram is similar to the QPSK modulation.

Problem Statement

Design and simulate the QAM modulator with different constellations in Commsim, and observe the signals at different intermediate blocks.

Procedure

1.   Design the QAM modulator as shown in Figure 12.01. Set the bit rate of the data source PN sequence (Comm>Signal Sources) to 1 bps.

2.   Connect the output of PN sequence to serial to parallel converter (Comm>Digital). Set bits per symbol of serial to parallel converter to 3.

3.   Use 1 Hz sinusoid signals (Comm>Signal Sources) for the carrier.

4.   Theoretically compute the I-channel and Q-channel amplitude values for different signal points in the constellation diagram for the 8-QAM (1.7) constellation.

It is better not to directly provide the simulation schematic to the students. The block diagram shown in Figure 12.01 describes the components required. It is better to let the students search through the various blocks available in Commsim and allow them to come up with their own design schematic.

After they complete the design, the schematics and result graphs may be supplied for comparison and verification.

You have already learned about the various possible constellation diagrams for 8-QAM in *Electronic Communication Systems I*. Use simple geometry to arrive at computing the I and Q magnitudes for different symbol levels, which are to be included in the IQ mapper data file.

Use simply geometry to arrive at the theoretical values of I and Q magnitudes for different 8-QAM constellations as shown in Figure 12.02.

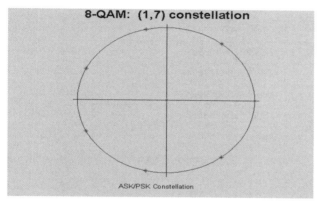

*Figure 12.02:   8-QAM (1, 7) Constellation Diagram

5.   Prepare an IQ mapper (Comm>Operators>IQ Mapper) data file (.dat extension) as described in the theory part of this lab, and specify it in the IQ mapper block parameters (either select the file or browse for it). Specify the number of constellation points in the constellation size parameter of the IQ mapper block.

Refer to the data file entries of 8-QAM (1, 7) constellation in Table 12.1 for the IQ mapper table. For more information on how to create the data file from this table, refer to theory section of this lab exercise.

Symbol level	I-Channel Amplitude	Q-Channel Amplitude
0	0	0
1	1	0
2	0.62348980185873	0.78183148246803
3	-0.22252093395631	0.97492791218182
4	-0.90096886790242	0.43388373911756
5	-0.90096886790242	-0.43388373911756
6	-0.22252093395631	-0.97492791218182
7	0.62348980185873	-0.78183148246803

Table 12.1: Data File Entries for 8-QAM (1, 7) Constellation

6. Run the simulation for the required time period so you can see the different bit combinations represented by the waveforms. Use the following simulation properties (Simulate>Simulation properties):

    Frequency: 100   End: 40

7. Plot the graphs at the output of each block, and analyze them.
8. Modify the schematic to simulate the (4, 4) 8-QAM constellation.

All you have to do is to use the same schematic and change the IQ mapper data file.

9. Theoretically compute the I-channel and Q-channel amplitude values for different signal points in the constellation diagram for the 8-QAM (4, 4) star constellation as shown in Figure 12.03.

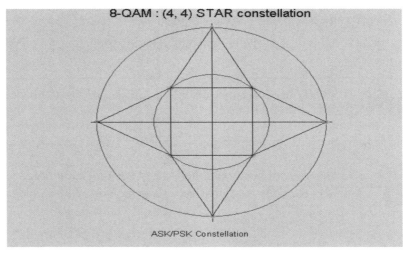

Figure 12.03: 8-QAM (4, 4) Star Constellation

 Refer to the IQ Mapping for 8-QAM (4, 4) star constellation in Table 12.2 for the IQ mapper table.

Symbol Level	I-Channel Amplitude	Q-Channel Amplitude
0	0.70710678118655	0.70710678118655
1	−0.70710678118655	0.70710678118655
2	−0.70710678118655	−0.70710678118655
3	0.70710678118655	−0.70710678118655
4	2	0
5	0	2
6	−2	0
7	0	−2

Table 12.2: IQ Mapping for 8-QAM (4, 4) Star Constellation

10. Repeat steps seven and eight.

11. Modify the schematic to simulate the triangular 8-QAM constellation.

Simply use the same schematic and change the IQ mapper data file.

---

12. Theoretically compute the I- and Q-channel amplitude values for different signal points in the constellation diagram for the 8-QAM triangle constellation as shown in Figure 12.04.

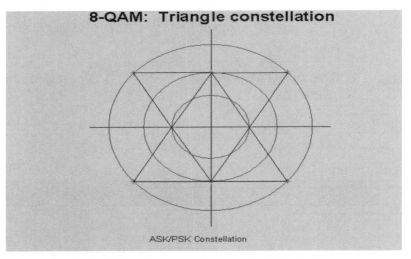

Figure 12.04: 8-QAM Triangle Constellation Diagram

Refer to the data file for IQ mapper (8-QAM triangle constellation) in Table 12.3.

Symbol Level	I-Channel Amplitude	Q-Channel Amplitude
0	0.5	0
1	−0.5	0
2	0	0.86602540378444
3	0	0.86602540378444
4	1	0.86602540378444
5	−1	0.86602540378444
6	−1	0.86602540378444
7	1	0.86602540378444

Table 12.3: Data File for IQ Mapper (8-QAM Triangle Constellation)

13. Repeat steps seven to nine.
14. Modify the schematic to simulate the square 8-QAM constellation.

 Simply use the same schematic and just change the IQ mapper data file.

15. Theoretically compute the I- and Q-channel amplitude values for different signal points in the constellation diagram for the 8-QAM square constellation. The constellation diagram is shown in Figure 12.05.

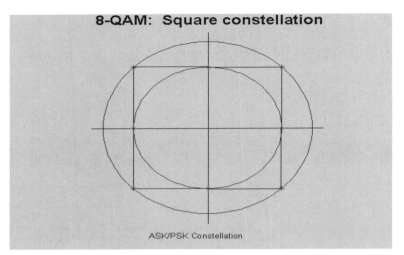

Figure 12.05: 8-QAM Square Constellation Diagram

 Refer to the data file for IQ mapper (8-QAM square constellation) in Table 12.4.

Symbol Level	I-channel Amplitude	Q-channel Amplitude
0	1	0
1	0	1
2	−1	0
3	0	−1
4	1	1
5	−1	1
6	−1	−1
7	1	−1

Table 12.4: Data File for IQ Mapper 8-QAM Square Constellation

16. Repeat steps seven and eight.

The level generator can be simulated using the IQ-mapper block available in Commsim. Here you can specify the signal constellation size. For example, it should be 8 for the present lab (8-QAM). The I and Q magnitudes for different 3-bit combinations can be specified in a data file with the extension .dat and loaded into the IQ mapper.

Conclusion/Observation

1. The working of the QAM modulation is simulated in Commsim and studied.

2. How did you design the IQ mapper in Commsim?

3. How can you change the QAM so that the signal points correspond to different constellations?

Solution

The outputs of the different blocks of the simulation schematic are shown in Figures 12.06 through 12.31.

The digital signal generated by the PN code generator is shown in Figure 12.06.

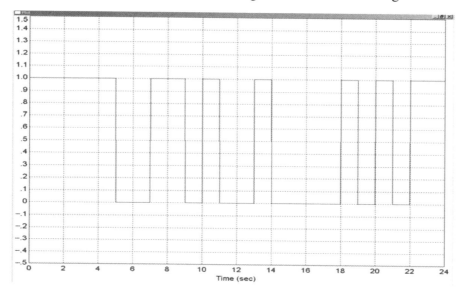

Figure 12.06: Digital Data Signal

The clock of this digital signal is shown in Figure 12.07.

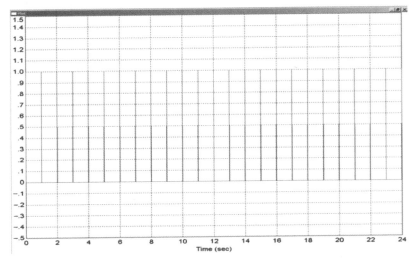

Figure 12.07: Digital Clock Signal

You can see that the bit rate is 1bps, which is the same as the PN code generator. In addition, the digital signal is Non-Return-to-Zero (NRZ) bipolar.

Figure 12.08 shows the output of the serial-to-parallel converter.

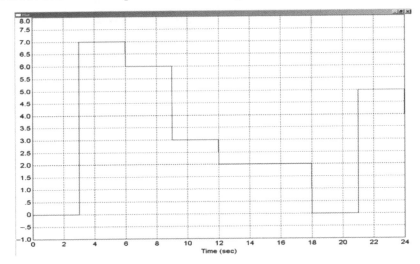

Figure 12.08: Serial-to-Parallel Converter Block Output

The output clock of the signal is shown in Figure 12.09.

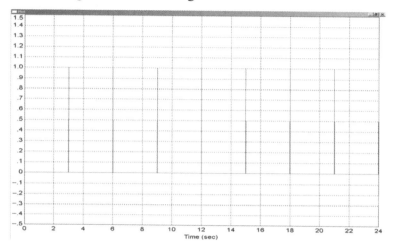

Figure 12.09: Serial-to-Parallel Converter Block Clock Signal

Figure 12.09 shows that the serial-to-parallel block clock signal is spaced three times wider on the time axis when compared to the original digital signal. Therefore, the data rate of the signal is reduced by one third. The output of the serial-to-parallel converter is similar to a level generator.

The output of the serial-to-parallel converter is given to the IQ mapper. The number of different bit combinations possible is given in the IQ mapper specification. For the current example, it is eight. The IQ mapper requires a data file that specifies the I-channel and Q-channel amplitudes for different bit combinations.

Figure 12.02 shows the constellation diagram for an 8-QAM (1, 7).

The magnitudes of the signal point in the X and Y directions are computed based on the constellation diagram. The X-amplitude gives the I-channel amplitude and the Y-amplitude gives the Q-channel amplitude. The data for the IQ mapper is obtained from the signal constellation.

.

Figure 12.10 shows the I-channel levels that were generated based on the input signal pattern.

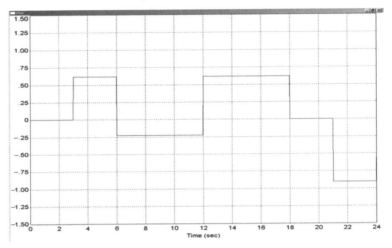

Figure 12.10: I-Channel Signal Amplitude Levels

Figure 12.11 shows the I-channel cosine carrier that is multiplied by the I-channel amplitude level signal.

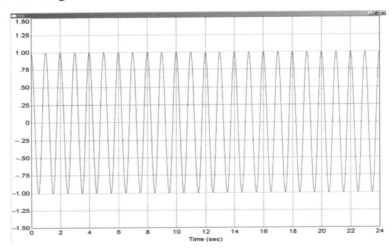

Figure 12.11: I-Channel Carrier Signal

Figure 12.12 shows the I-channel signal that is obtained by multiplying the I-channel carrier signal with the I-channel level signal.

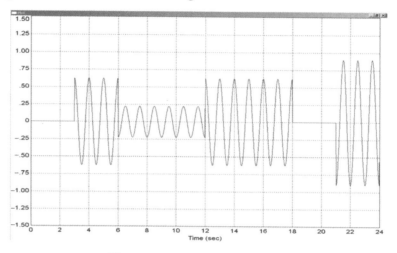

Figure 12.12: I-Channel Signal

Similarly, the Q-channel amplitude level signal is generated by the IQ mapper based on the input signal, as shown in Figure 12.13.

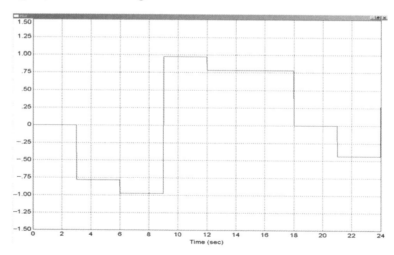

Figure 12.13: Q-Channel Amplitude Level

Figure 12.14 shows the final modulated Q-channel carrier signal.

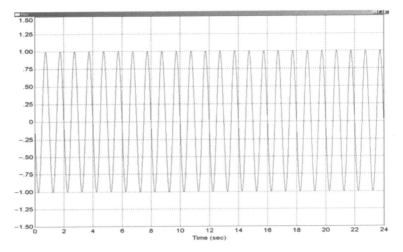

Figure 12.14: Q-Channel Carrier Signal

Figure 12.15 shows the Q-channel signal obtained by multiplying the Q-channel carrier signal with the Q-channel amplitude level signal.

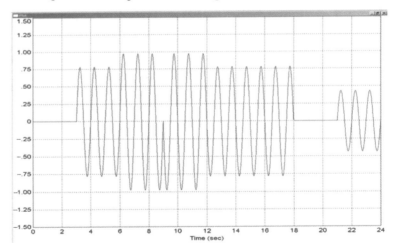

Figure 12.15: Q-Channel Signal

Figure 12.16 shows the QAM signal obtained by adding the I-channel signal and the Q-channel signal for the 8-QAM (1, 7) constellation.

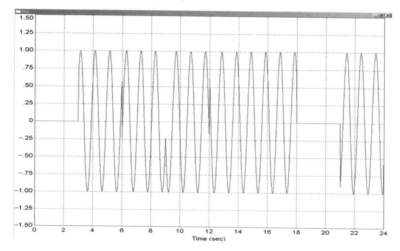

Figure 12.16: 8-QAM Signal for (1, 7) Constellation

You can see that the amplitude of the signal is also varied in addition to the changes in the phase. From the constellation, you can see that only the all-zero-bit combination has an amplitude of zero. All the remaining signal points have an amplitude of unity because they lie on the unit circle with different phases.

Figure 12.03 shows the constellation diagram for an 8-QAM (4, 4) star constellation.

To modify the QAM schematic to simulate the 8-QAM (4, 4) star constellation, change the data file specified in the IQ mapper block to the new data file with the specified values.

Figure 12.17 shows the I-channel amplitudes generated by the IQ mapper based on the input digital signal.

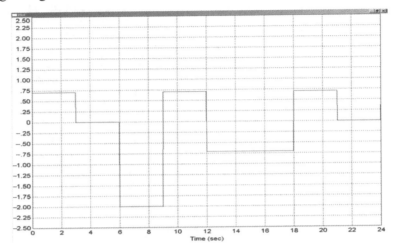

Figure 12.17: I-Channel Amplitude Level Signal

Figure 12.18 shows the I-channel signal output obtained by multiplying the amplitude level signal in Figure 12.17 with the I-channel carrier signal.

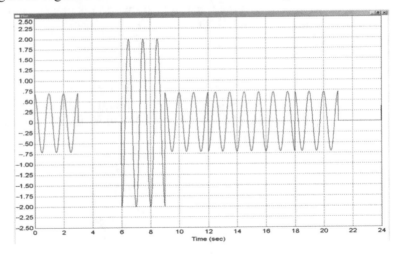

Figure 12.18: I-Channel Signal

The Q-channel amplitude signal generated by the IQ mapper block based on the input digital signal is shown in Figure 12.19.

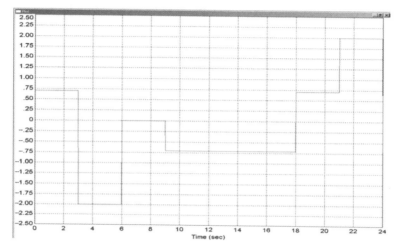

Figure 12.19: Q-Channel Amplitude Level Signal

Figure 12.20 shows the Q-channel signal obtained by multiplying the Q-channel amplitude level signal with the Q-channel carrier signal.

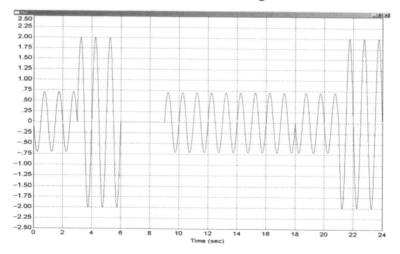

Figure 12.20: Q-Channel Signal

Figure 12.21 shows the final 8-QAM (4, 4) star constellation signal.

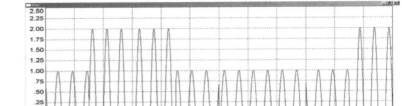

Figure 12.21: 8-QAM (4, 4) Star Constellation Final Output

You can see that both the amplitude and phase of the carrier are modulated.

 To modify the QAM schematic for simulating the 8-QAM triangle constellation, change the data file specified in the IQ mapper block to the new data file with the specified values.

Figure 12.22 shows the amplitude levels generated by the IQ mapper for the I-channel for the 8-QAM triangle constellation based on the input digital signal.

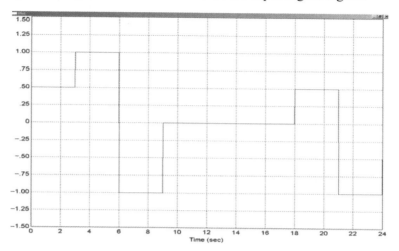

Figure 12.22: I-Channel Amplitude Level Signal

Figure 12.23 shows the I-channel signal obtained by multiplying the I-channel carrier signal with the I-channel amplitude level signal.

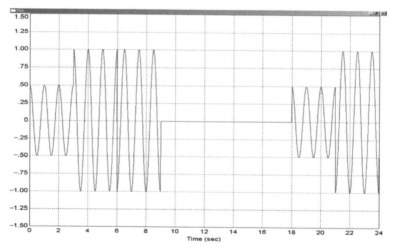

Figure 12.23: I-Channel Signal

Figure 12.24 shows the Q-channel amplitude level signal generated by the IQ mapper block based on the input digital signal.

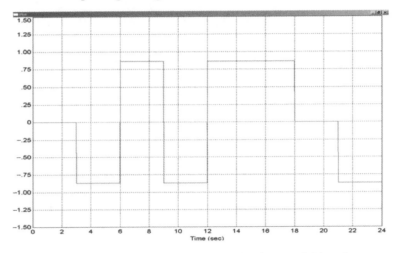

Figure 12.24: Q-Channel Amplitude Level Signal

Figure 12.25 shows the Q-channel signal obtained by multiplying the Q-channel carrier signal with the Q-channel amplitude level signal shown in Figure 12.24.

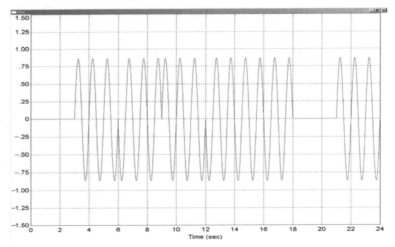

Figure 12.25: Q-Channel Signal

Figure 12.26 shows the final 8-QAM signal for the triangle constellation.

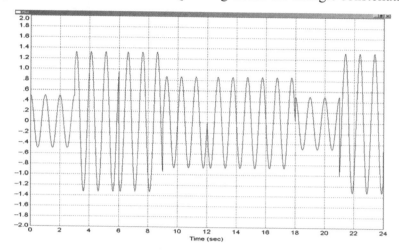

Figure 12.26: QAM Triangle Constellation Signal Output

You can see that the signal amplitude and phase is varied in accordance with the input digital signal.

To modify the QAM schematic for simulating the 8-QAM triangle constellation, change the data file specified in the IQ mapper block to the new data file with the specified values.

Figure 12.27 shows the amplitude levels generated by the IQ mapper for the I-channel of the 8-QAM square constellation, based on the input digital signal.

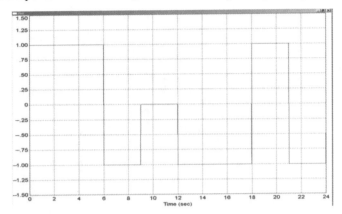

Figure 12.27: I-Channel Amplitude Level Signal

Figure 12.28 shows the I-channel signal obtained by multiplying the I-channel carrier signal with the I-channel amplitude level signal.

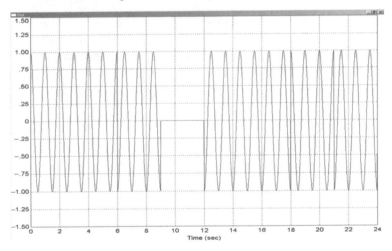

Figure 12.28: I-Channel Signal

Figure 12.29(a) shows the Q-channel amplitude level signal generated by the IQ mapper block based on the input digital signal.

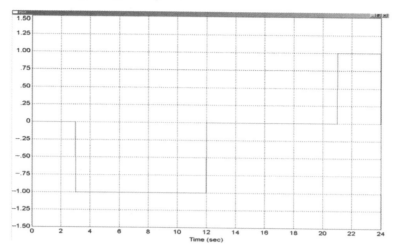

Figure 12.29(a): Q-Channel Amplitude Level Signal

Figure 12.29b shows the Q-channel signal obtained by multiplying the Q-channel carrier signal with the Q-channel amplitude level signal shown in Figure 12.29(a).

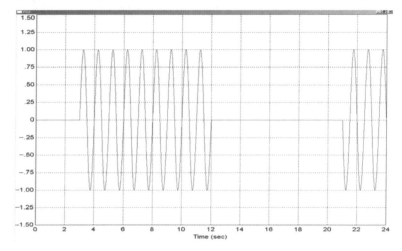

Figure 12.29(b): Q-Channel Signal

Figure 12.30 shows the final 8-QAM signal for the square constellation.

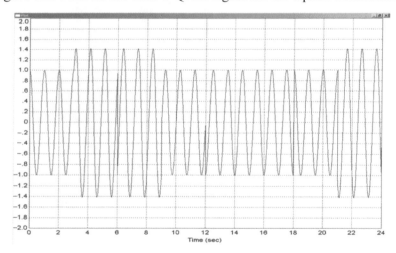

Figure 12.30: QAM Square Constellation Signal Output

You can see that both the amplitude and the phase are varied.

The IQ mapping data files for the four constellations are given in Tables 12.1, 12.2, 12.3, and 12.4.

Lab Activity Checklist

S. No.	Tasks	Completed	
		Yes	No
1.	QAM modulator is simulated in Commsim		
2.	8-QAM (1, 7) modulator is simulated in Commsim, and the signals at different blocks are observed and analyzed		
3.	8-QAM (4, 4) star modulator is simulated in Commsim, and the signals at different blocks are observed and analyzed		
4.	8-QAM triangle modulator is simulated in Commsim, and the signals at different blocks are observed and analyzed		
5.	8-QAM square modulator is simulated in Commsim, and the signals at different blocks are observed and analyzed		

Lab Exercise 13—Generation of PN Codes with a Modulo Shift Register

Objective

- Design the modulo shift register generator circuit to generate a PN noise code for a given primitive polynomial.
- Design and build the Multiple Shift Register Generation (MSRG) using D-flip flops on a proto board.
- Observe the generated PN code and verify the properties of the code generated.

Theory

The modulo shift register generator is one of the linear feedback shift register method for the generation of the PN codes for a given primitive polynomial. The primitive polynomial has a general form, as shown below:

$$P(x) = 1 + c_1 x^1 + c_2 x^2 + c_3 x^3 \dots\dots\dots c_{n-1} x^{n-1} + c_n x^n$$

Depending on the values of the coefficients of the primitive polynomial, it is decided whether to add modulo-2 addition or not. The general block diagram for MSRG implementation is shown in Figure 13.01.

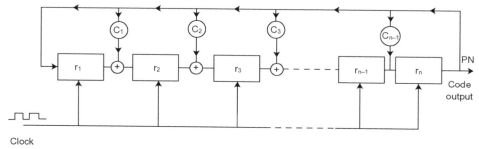

Figure 13.01: MSRG Generation of PN Codes

When $c_i = 0$, there is no modulo-2 addition after the register r_i, and the value stored in the register r_i is simply shifted to the register r_{i+1} with the clock input. On the other hand, if the value of $c_i = 1$, the modulo-2 addition of the value in the register r_i is performed with the value fed back from the register r_n as $r_i \oplus r_n$ and the result of the modulo-2 addition is shifted into the register r_{i+1}. The values of the coefficients of the primitive polynomial will determine the number and location of modulo-2 adders in the design circuit.

Problem Statement

Given the primitive polynomial $P(x) = 1 + x + x^3$ for MSRG PN code generation, design and build the circuit using D-flip flops on a protoboard and verify the properties of PN codes.

Lab Setup

S.No.	Part Description
1.	IC7474
2.	IC7486
3.	Clock generator
4.	DC voltage supply

Table 13.1: PN Code Lab Components

▨ Oscilloscope
▨ Probes and connecting wires

The design for the MSRG is shown in Figure 13.02.

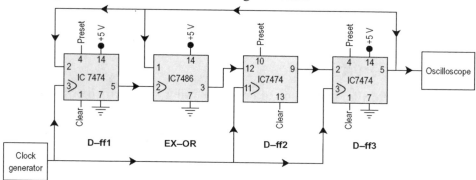

Figure 13.02: MSRG Generation of PN Codes

Procedure

1. Based on the primitive polynomial, design the Linear Feedback Shift register Multiple Shift Register Generation (LFSR MSRG) implementation block for generating the PN code.

2. Find the required number of LFSRs.

3. Find the number and location of the modulo-2 adders.

4. Use D-flip flops (IC7474) for shift registers and EX-OR gates (IC7486) to design the LFSR SSRG.

5. Study the different inputs needed for the D-flip flop. Initialize the registers to the following values:

$r_1 = 1, \ r_2 = 0$ and $r_3 = 0$

6. Theoretically compute the PN code that will be generated using the design.

7. Give the clock signal to all of the D-flip flops (IC7474).

8. Connect the clock input and the MSRG LFSR output to the oscilloscope.

9. Observe the PN code output for code length (previously calculated).

10. Compare the observed PN code with the theoretically computed PN code.

11. Plot the graphs.

12. Verify that the output of the LFSR will be a repeated, continuous sequence of the generated PN code (by observing the oscilloscope output for more than twice the code length).

13. Verify the following properties of the PN code:

a. Balance property

b. Slide window property

c. Run length property

Conclusion/Observation

▨ The MSRG generation of PN codes using the specified primitive polynomial is designed, built, and studied.

▨ How many shift registers/D-flip flops are required for the given primitive polynomial?

▨ How many EX-OR gates are required for the given primitive polynomial?

▨ How did you design the driving signal for the preset and clear inputs of the D-flip flops?

Solution

The following solution is simulated by Multisim simulator.

First from the primitive polynomial, design the theoretical circuit and find the theoretical PN code.

The order of the polynomial is 3. So the number of shift registers (D-flip flops) is 3.

The theoretical MSRG is shown in Figure 13.01.

Theoretical PN code generated is shown in Table 13.2.

	r_1	$r_1, r_3 = r_1 \oplus r_3$	r_2	r_3	PN code output
Initial state	1		0	0	
Clock 1	0	1,0 = 1	1	0	0
Clock 2	0	0,0 =0	0	1	0
Clock 3	1	0,1 = 1	1	0	1
Clock 4	0	1,0 =1	1	1	0
Clock 5	1	0,1 = 1	1	1	1
Clock 6	1	1,1 = 0	0	1	1
Clock 7	1	1,1 = 0	0	0	1
Theoretical PN code output	0 0 1 0 1 1 1				

Table 13.2: Theoretical PN code

The truth table for the D-flip in the Multisim software is given below in Table 13.3.

Preset (active low)	Clear (active low)	D	Q
0	1	1	1
1	0	0	0
1	1	a	a
1	1	b	b

Table 13.3: Truth Table

If you need to initialize the D-flip flop to a 1, you should give a preset = 0 and clear = 1 for a short time. The D-flip flop has to work according to the clock, and then the preset and clear should both be made 1.

If you want to initialize the D-flip flop to 0, then you should give preset = 1 and clear = 0 for a short time initially, and then change to preset = clear = 1 to make it work as shift register.

The two graphs for the preset_reset_input generator are shown in Figure 13.03.

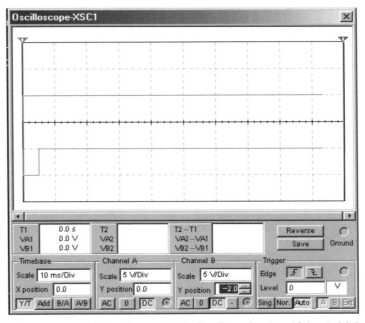

Figure 13.03: Signals for Preset and Clear Inputs for D-flip flops for Specifying Initial Conditions

The graphs presented here are obtained from the simulations done in the Multisim software.

The plots are just for verification purposes. All the graphs are sample graphs obtained from Multisim simulation of the hardware circuit presented previously.

The simulated PN code output as seen on the oscilloscope is shown in Figure 13.04.

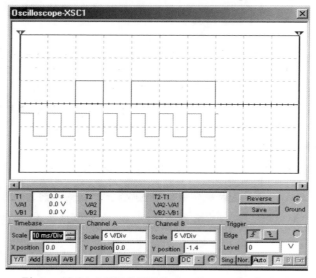

Figure 13.04: MSRG PN Codes Output for [1 0 0]

To verify the repetition of the PN code sequence, plot the graphs for two code-length time periods, as shown in Figure 13.05.

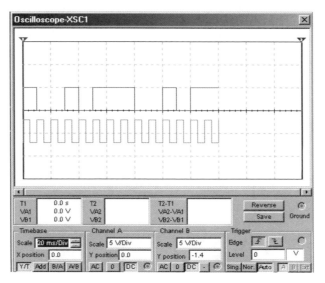

Figure 13.05: Repetition of PN Codes

Verify the following properties:

- Balance property
- Sliding window property
- Run length property

Lab Activity Checklist

S. No.	Tasks	Completed	
		Yes	No
1.	The MSRG circuit diagram is realized theoretically and the PN code is computed theoretically		
2.	The MSRG circuit is built on the protoboard using D-flip flops		
3.	The properties of PN codes are verified		

Lab Exercise 14—Generation of PN Codes with a Simple Shift Register

Objectives

- Design the Simple Shift Register Generator (SSRG) circuit to generate a PN noise code for a given MSRG primitive polynomial.
- Design and build the SSRG using D-flip flops on a protoboard.
- Verify if the same PN code (shifted version) generated is the same as the one generated using MSRG in lab exercise 13.

Theory

The modulo shift register generator is one of the Linear Feedback Shift Register (LFSR) methods for the generation of the PN code, for a given primitive polynomial. The primitive polynomial has a general form, as shown below:

$$P(x) = 1 + c_1x^1 + c_2x^2 + c_3x^3 \ldots \ldots \ldots c_{n-1}x^{n-1} + c_nx^n$$

If the primitive polynomial is given for MSRG, the corresponding reciprocal primitive polynomial for SSRG implementation can be found using the following transformation: $P'(x) = x^n P(x^{-1})$.

Depending on the values of the coefficients of the primitive polynomial, it is decided whether or not to add modulo-2 addition.

The general block diagram for SSRG implementation is shown in Figure 14.01.

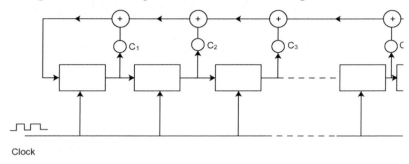

Clock

Figure 14.01: SSRG Generation of PN Codes

When $c_i = 0$, there is no modulo-2 addition after the register r_i, and the value stored in the register r_i is simply shifted to the register r_{i+1} with the clock input. If the value of $c_i = 1$, the modulo-2 addition of the value in the register r_i is performed with the value fed back from the register r_n as $r_i \oplus r_n$, and the result of the modulo-2 addition is shifted into the register r_{i+1}. The values of the coefficients of the primitive polynomial will determine the number and location of modulo-2 adders in the design circuit.

Problem Statement

The primitive polynomial is $P(x) = 1 + x + x^3$ for MSRG PN code generation. Design the SSRG circuit using D-flip flops, and verify that the same PN code is generated.

Lab Setup

DPSK Parts - S.No.	Part Description
1.	IC7474
2.	IC7486
3.	Clock generator
4.	DC voltage supply

Table 14.1: PN Code Lab Components

1. Oscilloscope
■ Probes and connecting wires

The design for the SSRG is given in the Figure 14.02.

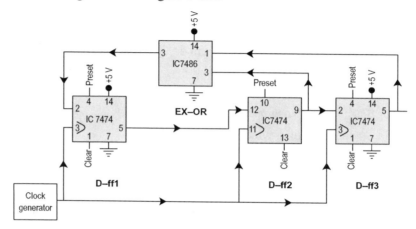

Figure 14.02: SSRG Generator

Procedure

1. Based on the primitive polynomial given for MSRG, find the corresponding SSRG primitive polynomial and design the LFSR SSRG implementation block for generating the PN code.

   a. Find the number of required LFSRs.

   b. Find the number and location of the modulo-2 adders.

2. Use D-flip flops (IC7474) for shift registers and EX-OR gates (IC7486) for building the circuit.

3. Study the different inputs needed for the D-flip flop. Initialize the registers to the following values:

$r_1 = 1, \ r_2 = 0$ and $r_3 = 0$

4. Theoretically compute the PN code that will be generated using the design and compare the theoretical PN code for SSRG with theoretical PN code for MSRG obtained in the previous lab exercise. Comment on the result.

5. Give the clock signal to all of the D-flip flops.

6. Connect the clock input and the SSRG LFSR output to the CRO.

7. Observe the PN code output for code length (previously calculated).

8. Compare the observed PN code with the theoretically computed PN code.

9. Compare the SSRG CRO PN code output with MSRG CRO PN code output obtained in lab exercise 13.

10. Plot the graphs.

11. Verify that the output of LFSR is a repeated continuous sequence of the generated PN code. You can do this by observing the Oscilloscope output for more than twice the code length.

12. Verify the following parameters:

   *Balance property

   *Sliding window property

   *Run time property

Conclusion/Observation

▨ The SSRG generation of PN codes using the specified MSRG primitive polynomial is realized on a protoboard using ICs.

▨ What will be the order of the polynomial in SSRG implementation compared to the MSRG to generate the same PN code?

▨ Is the PN code produced by the SSRG exactly the same as the one produced using the MSRG? Or are there any phase shifts?

Solution

Find the reciprocal primitive polynomial for SSRG that will generate the same PN code from the given MSRG primitive polynomial.

It is obtained from the following transformation:

$$P'(x) = x^n P(x^{-1})$$

The given primitive polynomial for MSRG is $P(x) = 1 + x + x^3$.

The corresponding SSRG reciprocal primitive polynomial is obtained as:

$$P'(x) = x^3 P(x^{-1})$$

$$= x^3 \left(1 + \frac{1}{x} + \frac{1}{x^3} \right)$$

$$= 1 + x^2 + x^3$$

Next find the theoretical circuit and the theoretical PN code.

The order of the polynomial is 3. Therefore the number of shift registers (D-flip flops) is 3. The theoretical SSRG is shown in Figure 14.01. The theoretical PN code generated is shown in Table 14.2.

	r_1	r_2	r_3	$r_2, r_3 = r_1 \oplus r_3$	PN code output
Initial states	1	0	0		
Clock 1	0	1	0	1,0 = 1	0
Clock 2	1	0	1	0,0 =0	1
Clock 3	1	1	0	0,1 = 1	1
Clock 4	1	1	1	1,0 =1	1
Clock 5	0	1	1	0,1 = 1	0
Clock 6	0	0	1	1,1 = 0	0
Clock 7	1	0	0		1
Theoretical PN code output	0 1 1 1 0 0 1				

Table 14.2: Theoretical PN Code

The following is the result of the simulation of the design in Multisim.

The simulated PN code output as seen on the CRO is shown in Figure 14.03.

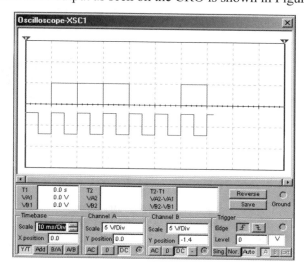

Figure 14.03: SSRG PN Codes Output [1 0 0]

To verify the repetition of the PN code sequence, plot the graphs for two code-length time periods, as shown in Figure 14.04. The output PN code as observed on the CRO is 0 1 1 1 0 0 1, same as the theoretically computed PN code. The PN code generated using the SSRG is also the same as MSRG.

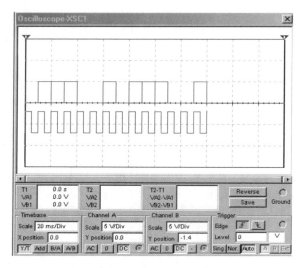

Figure 14.04: Repetition PN Codes for SSRG

Lab Activity Checklist

S. No.	Tasks	Completed	
		Yes	No
1.	The SSRG circuit diagram is realized theoretically and the PN code is computed theoretically		
2.	The SSRG circuit is built using D-flip flops on a protoboard		
3.	The PN code from reciprocal primitive polynomial of SSRG is the same as the one generated using MSRG		

Lab Exercise 15—Changing the Initial Values for a PN Code Generator

Objective

- Verify that a change in the initial values of the D-flip flop will result in the same PN code but with a phase shift for MSRG.
- Verify that a change in the initial values of the D-flip flop will result in the same PN code but with a phase shift for SSRG.

Problem Statement

Verify that a change in the initial values of the shift register will retain the same PN code with a possible phase shift for both MSRG and SSRG LFSR PN code generation methods.

Lab Setup

S. No.	Part Description
1.	IC7474
2.	IC7486
3.	Clock generator
4.	DC voltage supply

Table 15.1: PN Code Lab Components

- Oscilloscope
- Probes and connecting wires

Procedure for MSRG

1. Retain the MSRG circuit from Lab Exercise 13.
2. Change the initial values of the D-flip flop from [1 0 0] to [1 0 1].
3. Give the clock signal and observe the new PN code generated.
4. Compare it with the PN code generated in Lab Exercise 13.
5. Plot the graphs.

Procedure for SSRG

1. Retain the SSRG circuit from Lab Exercise 14.
2. Change the initial values of the D-flip flop from [1 0 0] to [1 0 1].
3. Give the clock signal and observe the new PN code generated.
4. Compare it with the PN code generated in Lab Exercise 14.
5. Plot the graphs.

Conclusion/Observation

- The effect of the initial values in the D-flip flop will result in a shifted version of the same PN code.
- What will happen if the initial values stored in all the D-flip flops are zeros?

Solution for MSRG

The theoretical PN code generated for MSRG is shown in Table 15.2.

	r_1	$r_1, r_3 = r_1 \oplus r_3$	r_2	r_3	PN code output
Initial states	1		0	1	
Clock 1	1	1,1 = 0	0	0	1
Clock 2	0	1,0 =1	1	0	0
Clock 3	0	0,0 = 0	0	1	0
Clock 4	1	0,1 =1	1	0	1
Clock 5	0	1,0 = 1	1	1	0
Clock 6	1	0,1 = 1	1	1	1
Clock 7	1	1,1 = 0	0	1	1
Theoretical PN code output		1 0 0 1 0 1 1			

Table 15.2: Theoretical PN Code

The simulated PN code in Multisim as seen on the oscilloscope is shown in Figure 15.01.

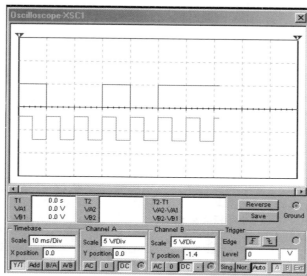

Figure 15.01: MSRG PN Codes Output [1 0 1]

Solution for SSRG

The theoretical PN code generated for SSRG is shown in Table 15.3.

	r_1	r_2	r_3	$r_2, r_3 = r_1 \oplus r_3$	PN code output
Initial states	1	0	1		
Clock 1	1	1	0	0,1 = 1	1
Clock 2	1	1	1	1,0 =0	1
Clock 3	0	1	1	1,1 = 0	0
Clock 4	0	0	1	1,1 =0	0
Clock 5	1	0	0	0,1 = 1	1
Clock 6	0	1	0	0,0 = 0	0
Clock 7	1	0	1	1,0 = 1	1
Theoretical PN code output	1 1 0 0 1 0 1				

Table 15.3: Theoretical PN Code

The simulated PN code output in Multisim as seen on the oscilloscope is shown in Figure 15.02.

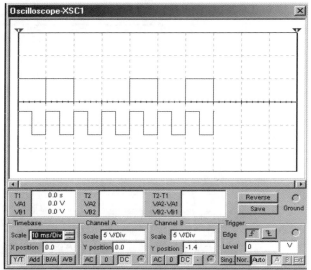

Figure 15.02: SSRG PN Codes Output [1 0 1]

Lab Activity Checklist

S. No.	Tasks	Completed	
		Yes	No
1.	Effect of change in the initial values of D-flip flop for MSRG LFSR is observed		
2.	Effect of change in the initial values of D-flip flop for SSRG LFSR is observed		

Lab Exercise 16—PN Codes: Study of Shift-and-Add Property

Objective

Verify the shift-and-add property of PN codes using D-flip flops.

Problem Statement

Verify the shift-and-add property of PN codes using the PN codes obtained from the MSRG LFSR and SSRG LFSR implementations in lab exercises 13 and 14.

Lab Setup

S. No.	Part Description
1.	IC7474
2.	IC7486
3.	Clock generator
4.	DC voltage supply

Table 16.1: PN Code Lab Components

▨ Oscilloscope

▨ Probes and connecting wires

Figure 16.01 shows a shift-and-add property verification circuit using MSRG and SSRG.

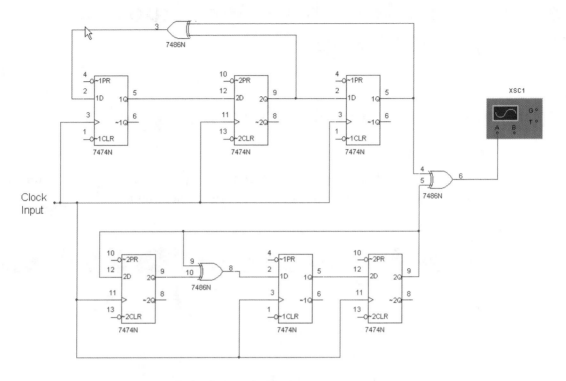

Figure 16.01: Shift-and-Add Property Verification Circuit Using MSRG

Procedure

1. Retain the MSRG schematic from Lab Exercise 13.

2. Retain the second SSRG circuit from Lab Exercise 14.

3. Connect the two circuits using a modulo-2 adder (EX-OR gate, i.e. IC7486), as shown in Figure 16.01.

4. Give the clock signal and observe the two input codes and the sum input code.

5. Verify if the result output code is a shifted version of the PN code generated using MSRG in Lab Exercise 13.

6. Plot the graphs.

Shifted versions of the PN code can be obtained by changing the initial values of the IC7474.

Conclusion/Observation

- The shift-and-add property of the PN codes is verified.
- How can you obtain a shifted version of a given PN code (realized by a given design)?
- What conclusion about code words can you make after verifying the shift-and-add property of the PN codes?

Solution

The theoretical PN code for the new initial values of the D-flip flops is shown in Table 16.2.

Clock	PN code 1 MSRG [1 0 0]	PN code 2 MSRG [1 0 1]	PN code 3 PN code 1 ⊗ PN code 2
Clock shift 1	0	1	1
Clock shift 2	0	0	0
Clock shift 3	1	0	1
Clock shift 4	0	1	1
Clock shift 5	1	0	1
Clock shift 6	1	1	0
Clock shift 1	1	1	0

Table 16.2: Theoretical PN Code

The simulated PN code output in Multisim, as seen on the oscilloscope, is shown in Fgures 16.02 and 16.03. Figure 16.02 shows the two individual codes and Figure 16.03 shows the sum of these two codes.

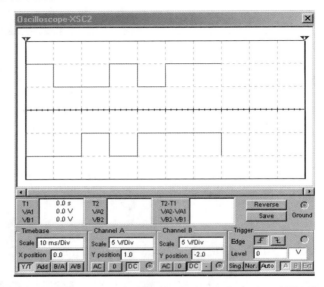

Figure 16.02 Shift-and-Add Property of PN Codes: PN Code 1 and PN Code 2

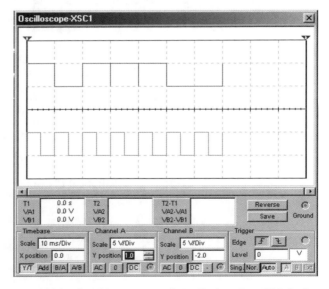

Figure 16.03: Shift-and-Add Property of PN Codes: Sum PN Code

Lab Activity Checklist

S. No.	Tasks	Completed	
		Yes	No
1.	The shift-and-add property of the PN codes is verified		

 All the theoretical parts of MSRG and SSRG design, theoretical PN code computation, and the verification of the PN code properties can be done as prelab activities.

Lab Exercise 17—Baseband DSSS Transmitting and Receiving Systems

Objective

- Simulate the baseband Direct Sequence Spread Spectrum (DSSS) transmitting system in Commsim.
- Simulate the baseband DSSS receiving system in Commsim.
- Study the working of the baseband DSSS transmitting and receiver systems in Commsim.
- Observe the effect of using a different PN code at the receiver for the recovery of the data.

Lab Setup

- PC with Commsim software.

Theory

In baseband DSSS transmitting system the low bit rate digital data is directly multiplied with the relatively high chip rate PN code data. This multiplication causes the signal to spread in its frequency spectrum. The resulting spread spectrum output is transmitted into the channel.

At the receiver end, the received signal is directly multiplied with the same PN code that is used at the transmitter, yielding recovery of the digital data. If a PN code other than the one used at the transmitter is used at the receiver end, then the signal decoded will appear as noise. A Commsim diagram of the baseband DSSS transmitter and receiver system is shown in Figure 17.01.

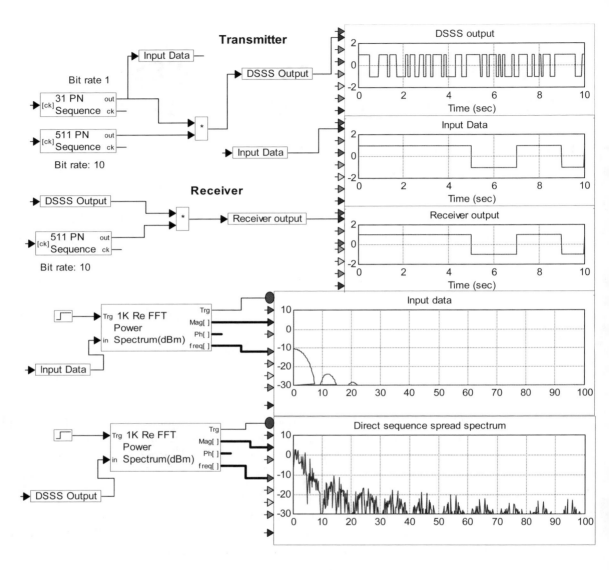

*Figure 17.01: Baseband DSSS Transmitter and Receiver System

Problem Statement

Simulate and study the working of the baseband DSSS transmitter and receiver system in Commsim.

Procedure

1. Set up the circuit in Commsim as shown in Figure 17.01. Use a PN code generator (Comm>Signal sources) as the digital data source at a low bit rate of 1 bps. Set the output to bi-level (-1, +1) and timing into internal.

2. Use another PN code generator block to generate the high bit rate spreading code. Set the bit rate of this PN generator to 10bps, bi-level and internal timing.

3. Give the digital data and the PN code data to the multiplier unit (Blocks>Arithmetic) to generate the DSSS output.

4. At the baseband DSSS receiver system, multiply the received signal with the same PN code (with the same bit rate) used at the transmitting end.

5. Use variables (Blocks>Annotations>Variable) to avoid crowded wiring and name them properly.

6. Observe the time domain of the baseband digital signal, the PN code, and the DSSS data.

7. Use the real-spectrum analyzer block (Comm>Operators>Spectrum real>) to observe the spectrum of the signals. Set the following settings for this unit:

> Trigger mode: Continuous
>
> Spectral Output: Mag/Phase
>
> FFT window type: Rectangular
>
> FFT size: 1 K
>
> Power Spectrum Unit: dBm
>
> Load: 50 ohms
>
> Output Frequency unit: Hz

8. Connect the Spectrum analyzer block to display unit. Use the following setting for the display unit.

> Fixer Bound
>
> External trigger: 0;
>
> XY Plot X=axis: 4
>
> Y-Upper Bound: 10   X-Upper Bound: 100
> Y- Lower Bound: -30   X- Lower Bound: 0

9. Simulate the circuit, and run the design. Use the following simulation properties (Simulate>Simulation Properties):

> Frequency: 200 Hz   End: 10

10. Observe the output and plot the graphs of input data, received signal, DSSS output and compare the frequency spectrum of the data and DSSS output.

11. To study the output received by an unintended signal trapper, use a PN code different from the one used by the transmitter end to decode the received signal. Analyze your observation.

12. Observe and compare the decoded signal with the original digital data encoded at the transmitting end.

Conclusion/Observation

- What happens to the spectrum of the digital signal after multiplication with the spreading code?
- What is the effect of re-multiplying the spread spectrum signal with the same PN code at the receiver? How does the spectrum of the resulting product signal compare with the original digital signal spectrum?
- What is the effect of using a different PN code at the receiver?
- How does the spectrum of the despread signal using the incorrect PN code compare with that of the original digital signal?

Solution

Figure 17.02 shows the digital data encoded at the transmitting end of the baseband DSSS transmitter system.

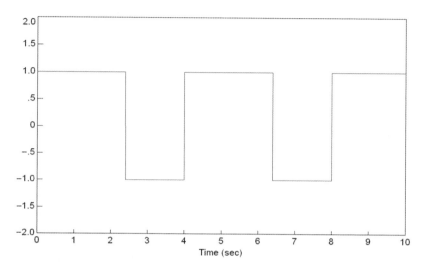

Figure 17.02: Digital Data Sequence at 0.25 bps (Hz)

Figure 17.03 shows the one-sided spectrum of the digital data at the transmitting end.

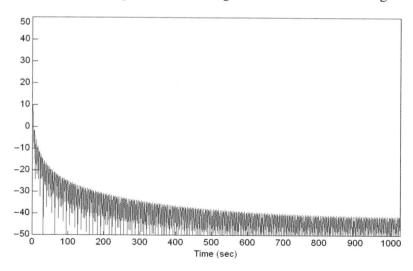

Figure 17.03: Spectrum of Digital Data at the Transmitting End

Figure 17.04 shows the PN code used for spreading at the transmitting end. The number of bits is high compared to the digital data being encoded.

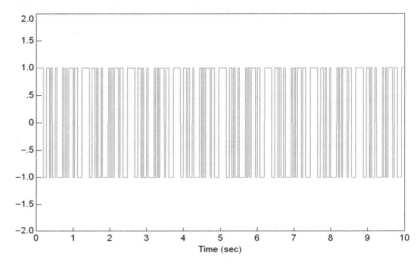

Figure 17.04: PN Code Used at the Transmitting End for Spreading

Figure 17.05 shows the spectrum of the PN code used for spreading at the transmitting end. Compared to the digital data, the spectrum is very wide.

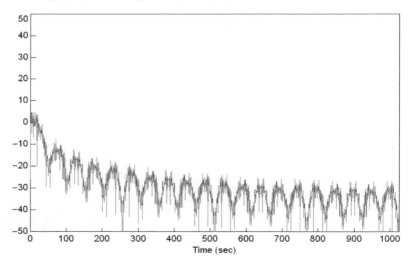

Figure 17.05: One-sided Spectrum of PN Code Used at the Transmitting End for Spreading

Figure 17.06 shows the output of the DSSS transmitter.

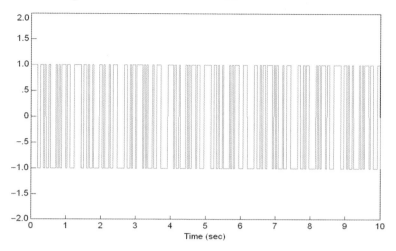

Figure 17.06: Baseband DSSS Transmitter Output

The bit rate is increased. Figure 17.07 shows the spectrum of the baseband DSSS transmitted signal. The spectrum of the digital signal is spread across a wide bandwidth after multiplication with the spreading PN code.

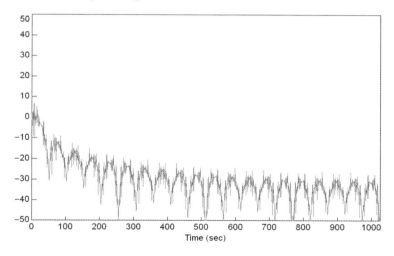

Figure 17.07: Spectrum of Baseband DSSS Transmitting System

Figure 17.08 shows the digital data that is recovered when the correct PN code is used at the baseband DSSS receiver system. The PN code used is the same as that used at the transmitting system. The original digital data is plotted with some time delay and attenuation in to distinguish the encoded and decoded data.

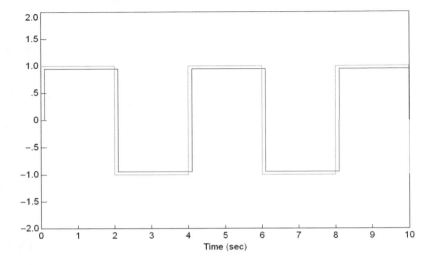

*Figure 17.08: Digital Data Recovered at DSSS Receiver Using Correct PN Code
Compared to Encoded Digital Data

Figure 17.09 shows the spectrum of the recovered digital data at the receiver.

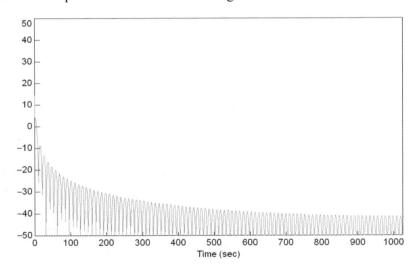

Figure 17.09: Spectrum of Recovered Digital Data at the DSSS Receiver System

Figure 17.10 shows a different PN code (generated using a 4-stage LFSR with initial conditions 1111).

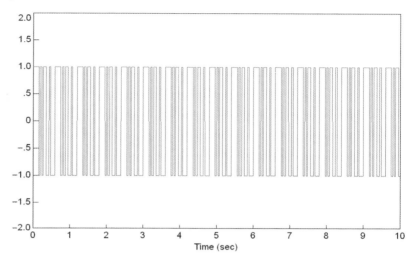

Figure 17.10: Incorrect PN Code Used for Demodulation at the Receiver

The spectrum of this different PN code is shown in Figure 17.11. Since the chip rate of this PN code is similar to that of the previous correct PN code, the spectrum of the signal appears similar.

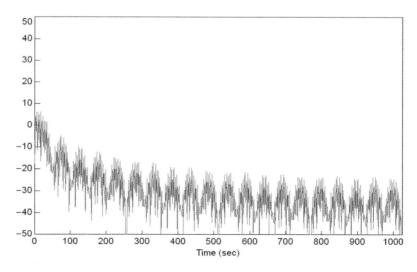

Figure 17.11: Spectrum of Incorrect PN Code

Figure 17.12 shows the digital data recovered using the second PN code. It is not similar to the original encoded data and so appears as just noise to the receiver.

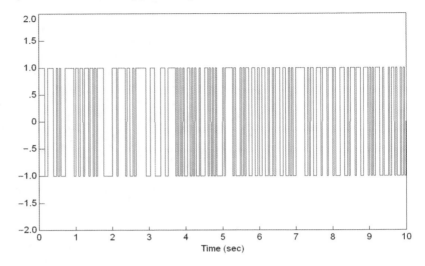

Figure 17.12: Decoded Digital Signal Using Incorrect PN Code

The spectrum of the incorrectly decoded digital signal is shown in Figure 17.13. The signal spectrum is also completely different from the original digital signal.

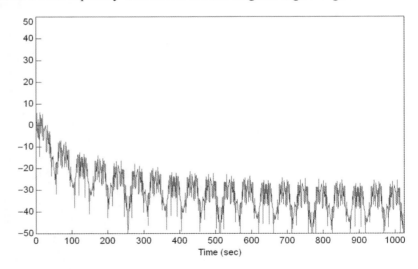

Figure 17.13: Spectrum of Decoded Signal Using Incorrect PN Code

Lab Activity Checklist

S. No.	Tasks	Completed	
		Yes	No
1.	Simulated baseband DSSS transmitting system		
2.	Simulated baseband DSSS receiver system		
3.	Studied the effect of using an incorrect PN code for despreading at the receiver end		

Lab Exercise 18—BPSK DSSS Transmitting and Receiving Systems

Objective

- Simulate the BPSK DSSS transmitting system in Commsim.
- Simulate the BPSK DSSS receiving system in Commsim.
- Study the working of BPSK DSSS transmitting and receiving systems in Commsim.

Lab Setup

- PC with Commsim software

Theory

The baseband DSSS studied in the previous lab is seldom used. The BPSK DSSS is the most commonly used DSSS system in modern digital communication systems.

For BPSK modulation an additional carrier block is used to modulate the digital data. Then this BPSK-modulated signal is multiplied with the high bit rate spreading code. The multiplication with the PN code can be done either before or after BPSK modulation of the data. In the present lab, the digital data is first BPSK modulated before the spreading code is applied.

A block diagram of the BPSK DSSS Transmitter and receiver system is shown in Figure 18.01. Since the PN code is multiplied at a later stage in the transmitting system, the received signal is first despread using the PN code. The resulting signal is then BPSK demodulated using integrate and dump block in the BPSK receiver.

Problem Statement

Simulate and study the BPSK DSSS transmitting and receiving systems using Commsim.

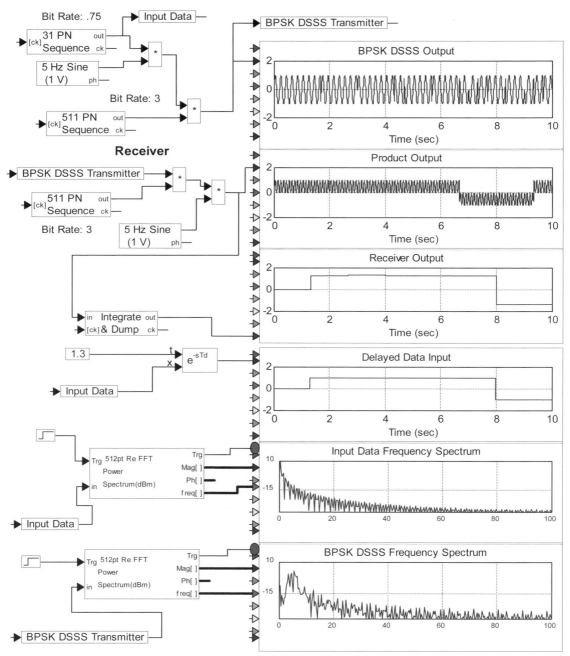

*Figure 18.01: BPSK DSSS Transmitter and Receiver System

Procedure

1. Set up the circuit in Commsim as shown in Figure 18.01.

2. Use a PN sequence block (Comm>Signal sources) at a bit rate of .75 as the digital data. Set the output mode into Bilevel (-1, +1) and internal timing.

3. Use a sinusoid (Comm> Signal sources) of frequency 3Hz as the carrier for the BPSK modulation.

4. Multiply the digital data and the carrier to obtain the BPSK-modulated output. The multiplier unit is located at Blocks> Arithmetic.

5. Multiply the high bit rate spreading PN code with the BPSK-modulated waveform to obtain the DSSS output. Choose the following settings for the PN code.

Shift register size: 9   Output mode: Bilevel (-1, +1)

Bit Rate (bps): 3   Timing: Internal

6. Steps 1 through 6 conclude the basic BPSK DSSS transmitter.

To simulate the BPSK DSSS receiver system in Commsim follow the steps given below. In order to avoid crowded wires use variables (Blocks>Annotation) and name them properly.

7. Give the received signal and the PN code to the multiplier for despreading the received signal. Use similar PN sequence for despreading.

8. Multiply the carrier signal with the despread signal to obtain the product signal. Use similar carrier signal for the product.

9. Give this product signal to the integrate-and-dump (Comm>Operators) circuit to recover the digital data. Use the following settings:

Rest value: 0   Scale Factor: 2   Dump timing: Internal

Output Mode: Held   Dump rate: 0.75   Initial Delay(sec): 0

10. In order to compare the original data with the demodulated data use a delay unit (Blocks> Time Delay>) to delay the input data. This delay is needed because of the delay in the integrate and dump unit. Delay the input data by around 1.3 sec.

11. Use the spectrum block (real) (Comm> Operators> Spectrum real) to obtain the spectrum of the input data and BPSK DSSS signals. Set the following for this unit:

    Trigger mode: Continuous   Spectral Output: Mag/Phase

    FFT window type: Rectangular   FFT size: 512

    Power Spectrum Unit: dBm   Load: 50 ohms

    Output Frequency unit: Hz

12. Connect the Spectrum analyzer block to display. Use the following setting for the display unit.

    Fixer Bound

    External trigger: 0;

    XY Plot X=axis: 4

    Y-Upper Bound : 10   X-Upper Bound : 100

    Y- Lower Bound: -35   X- Lower Bound: 0

13. Simulate the circuit, and run the design. Use the following simulation Properties (Simulate>Simulation Properties):

    Frequency: 200Hz

    End: 10

14. Compare the demodulated data with the original digital data.

15. Compare the frequency spectrum of the data and the BPSK DSSS.

16. Connect the display unit to different outputs and compare those with your analysis.

Conclusion/Observation

  ▪ The BPSK DSSS spread spectrum system is simulated and studied in Commsim.

  ▪ Why does the spectrum of the digital signal not contain even a single frequency peak like the BPSK carrier signal?

  ▪ Can you create the demodulator using a correlation block instead of the integrate-and-dump circuit?

Solution

Figure 18.02 shows the digital data that is given as input to the BPSK DSSS system.

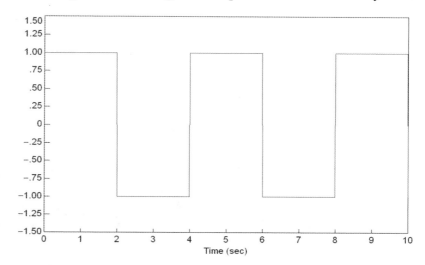

Figure 18.02: Digital Data

Figure 18.03 shows the spectrum of the digital data that is given to the BPSK DSSS system.

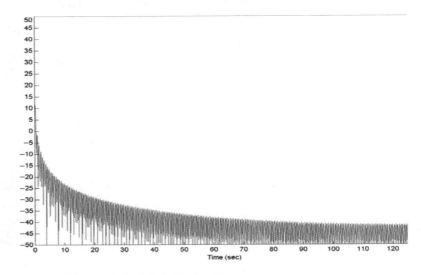

Figure 18.03: Digital Data Spectrum

Figure 18.04 shows the BPSK carrier.

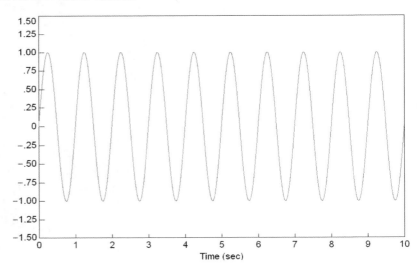

Figure 18.04: BPSK Carrier

Figure 18.05 shows the spectrum of the BPSK carrier multiplied with the digital data.

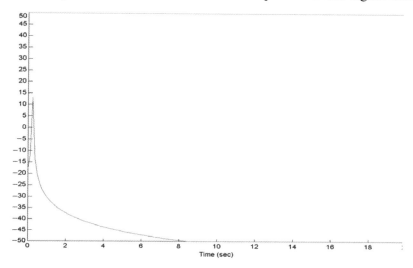

Figure 18.05: BPSK Carrier Spectrum

Figure 18.06 shows the BPSK-modulated signal before spreading.

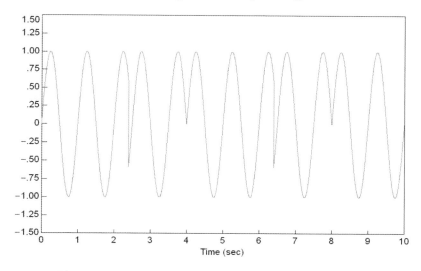

Figure 18.06: BPSK-Modulated Signal

Figure 18.07 shows the spectrum of the BPSK-modulated signal.

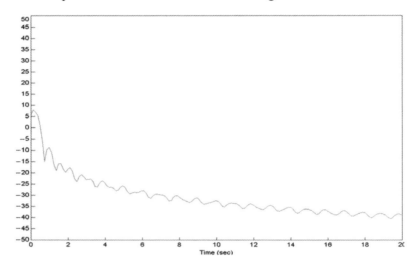

Figure 18.07: BPSK Output Spectrum

Figure 18.08 shows the output obtained by multiplying the BPSK-modulated signal with the PN code data.

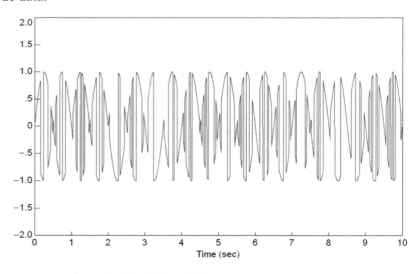

Figure 18.08: BPSK DSSS Output

The spectrum of the BPSK DSSS signal is shown in Figure 18.09. The signal spectrum is widened as a result of multiplication with the spreading code.

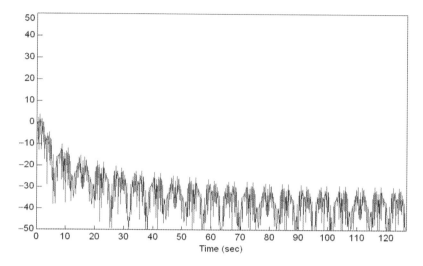

Figure 18.09: Spectrum of DSSS BPSK Output

Figure 18.10 shows the output of the despreading at the BPSK DSSS receiver when the correct PN code is used.

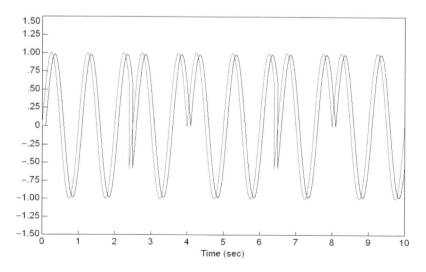

Figure 18.10: Despread Signal Compared to Transmitter BPSK Signal

The despreading has given the BPSK signal as output when the correct PN code was used. Figure 18.11 shows the spectrum of the despread signal.

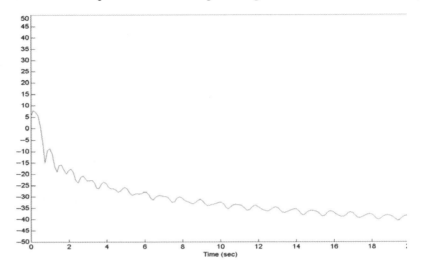

Figure 18.11: Despread Signal Spectrum

Figure 18.12 shows the signal obtained from multiplying the despread signal with the BPSK carrier signal at the receiver end. The original digital data is also superimposed to show the effect of this multiplication.

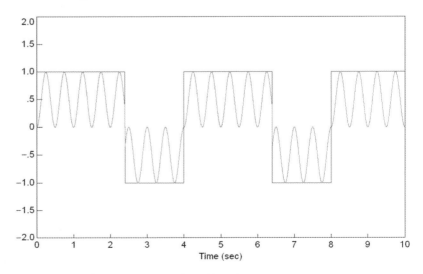

Figure 18.12: Product Signal

Figure 18.13 shows the BPSK-demodulated output for the integrate-and-dump circuit. It is compared to the original digital signal encoded at the transmitting end.

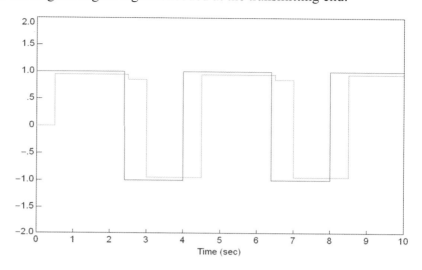

Figure 18.13: Final Demodulated Output

The output of the integrate-and-dump circuit is a bit delayed as the output of the integrate-and-dump receiver is obtained at the end of each symbol period.

Lab Activity Checklist

S. No.	Tasks	Completed	
		Yes	No
1.	BPSK DSSS transmitting system is simulated in Commsim and its working is studied		
2.	BPSK DSSS receiver system is simulated in Commsim and its working is studied		

Glossary

A

Acquisition time: Time taken to tract the received signal and lock the carrier signal to the incoming signal for proper synchronization between the transmitter and the receiver.

Additive White Gaussian Noise (AWGN): The noise inherent in all communication systems. It has a uniform and continuous frequency spectrum over a specified frequency band.

ALOHA: A multiple access protocol, which allows the users to transmit as soon as they have data. In case of successful reception at the end, next data is sent. In case of collision, the same data is retransmitted.

Amplitude shift keying: A digital modulation technique in which the amplitude of the carrier signal is modulated according to the digital signal.

Antenna gain: A measure of the directionality of the antenna or its capability to concentrate power in a preferred direction. It is directly proportional to the aperture area of the antenna and the square of the transmission frequency.

Antijam performance: The performance of a technique or a system to effectively combat a jammer signal.

Autocorrelation: Correlation carried out between a signal and the time-shifted version of the same signal.

B

Band-limited: A signal or a channel in which the frequencies present are restricted to be present in a fixed-frequency band.

Binary modulation: A digital modulation technique in which the number of symbol waveforms used to represent the digital signal is two.

Bit synchronization: The process of organizing un-synchronous bit streams arriving at different times at a node into a synchronized bit pattern.

C

Capture range: Once the PLL is locked, the range of frequencies over which it will maintain the lock is known as capture range.

Carrier: A high frequency signal served as the transport of the information-carrying baseband signal.

Carrier Sense Multiple Access (CSMA): A random multiple access protocol, devised to reduce collisions between users by adopting the users to sense the carrier before transmitting their data.

Carrier synchronization: The synchronization of frequency and phase of the locally generated reference signal and the received signal in a communication system.

Chip: The smallest time sequence in a pseudo noise sequence.

Chip rate: The bit or data rate of the spreading code.

Ciphers: The encrypted form of plain text.

CNR: The quantitative measure of a modulated carrier signal in relation to the noise level.

Code Division Multiple Access (CDMA): A multiple access technique in which each of the transmitters is given a unique code, which is a pseudonoise sequence, with which it modulates the information signal and sends it over the channel. All the transmitters can access the entire available bandwidth for all time.

Correlation: A measure of the extent to which two signals covary over a given period.

Correlator receiver: A digital modulation receiver system that makes use of a correlator to demodulate the received signal.

Cross correlation: Correlation evaluated between two different signals.

Cryptography: The study of ways to disguise messages to avert unauthorized interception.

D

Data Encryption Standard (DES): A block encryption system with an alphabet size of 2^{64} symbols. An input block of 64 bits, regarded as a plain text symbol in this alphabet, is replaced with a new cipher text symbol.

Demand Assigned Multiple Access (DAMA): A multiple access technique in which the communication resource is allocated to the users based on the demand and traffic flow.

Direct-Sequence Spread Spectrum (DSSS): An SS (spread spectrum) technique in which the digital data is directly multiplied with the spreading code to achieve spreading of the spectrum.

Dispersive delay line: A type of filter used in pulsed FM systems to accumulate, assemble, and release the energy received over an interval in a single burst.

Down converter: The component that receives the modulated RF (radio frequency) carrier and translates the RF in the downlink frequency spectrum of the satellite to the IF (intermediate frequency). Down conversion is usually accomplished in dual conversion process.

Downlink: The signal path between satellite and earth.

E

Earth station: The facility encompassing the transmitter and receiver sections of a satellite communication link at a particular geographic location.

Entropy: The average amount of information message.

Envelope detection: A technique is used to obtain the envelope of the matched filter output to be sent to the threshold detector in a digital modulation receiver.

Equivalent Isotropic Radiated Power (EIRP): A measure of radiated or transmitted power of an antenna gain and the power fed to the antenna input. EIRP $=P_t$ (in dBW) + G_t (in dB). EIRP is the transmitter power required to be fed to an isotropic antenna to give the same result as the transmitter and the antenna under consideration. Although the EIRP is defined and measured at the transmitter antenna, its practical significance is at the receiving end of the link. EIRP of the earth station transmitting antenna can be used to compute the power received by the satellite under a variety of transmission path conditions. Similarly, EIRP of satellite's transmitting antenna can be used to compute power received at the earth station.

Error correction: A technique that can effectively detect and correct bit errors introduced by the channel at the receiver.

F

Frame synchronization: Synchronization of the decoded raw bit pattern into different frames.

Frequency Division Multiple Access (FDMA): A multiple access technique in which the available bandwidth is divided into narrow channels, and each channel is allocated to a particular user, thereby enabling all the users to access the common communication channel.

Frequency Division Multiplexing (FDM): A technique in which different carrier frequencies are used to send different signals over the same available bandwidth.

Frequency-Hopped Spread Spectrum (FHSS): An SS (spread spectrum) technique in which the spreading code is used to synthesize frequencies, which are then used to spread the digital data spectrum.

Frequency reuse: The utilization of one carrier frequency in both vertical and horizontal polarization mode of transmission, using two sets of polarized parabolic reflector antenna.

Frequency Shift Keying (FSK): A digital modulation technique in which the frequency of the carrier signal is modulated according to the digital signal.

G

Global Positioning System (GPS): A satellite-based system that uses spread spectrum technique to spatially locate a user by specifying its altitude, longitude, and latitude.

Gold code: A code that is obtained by modulo-2 addition two different maximal length sequences.

H

Hamel basis: A set of vectors in a vector space that are linearly independent and can be used to obtain every signal possible in the vector space by a linear combination among them.

Hard-decision decoding: A type of decoding where the decision on the received signal is made from a set of fixed discrete possibilities.

High-Power Amplifier (HPA): An amplifier that is capable of delivering high power output (high gain).

J

Jammer: An intentional or unintentional coherent, unwanted disturbance to the desired signal, usually in the same frequency band of the desired signal.

K

Kasami code: A code obtained by modulo-2 adding a maximal length sequence and a decimated version of the same maximal length sequence.

L

Linear Feedback Shift Register (LFSR): A shift register converted into a pseudo random sequence generator by including a feedback loop.

Low Noise Amplifier (LNA): An amplifier with low noise.

M

M-ary modulation: A digital modulation technique in which multiple bits are combined to form symbols that can be represented by symbol waveforms in order to increase the bandwidth efficiency of the system.

Matched filter: A linear filter that is used in communication receivers to detect waveforms or bits.

Matched filter receiver: A digital modulation receiver system that makes use of the matched filter to demodulate the received signal.

Multimedia synchronization: A type of synchronization that takes care of the relative time synchronization between different types of media in a multimedia system.

Multipath: The different paths that a signal can take while propagating from the transmitter to the receiver in a terrestrial communication system. It specifies the mixed signal that is obtained by adding those different path signals.

N

Near-far problem: Arises when a jammer signal with high power levels intercepts the reception of a weak desired signal at the receiver.

Network synchronization: Synchronization of the clock inputs for various terminals and devices in a networked communication system.

Noise figure (F): A quantitative method of establishing receiver performance in terms of equivalent noise temperature.

O

Orthonormal vectors: A set of vectors that are mutually orthogonal and have unit length.

P

Packet synchronization: Synchronization of packets from the source node to the destination node when different packets take different routes while traveling from the source node to the destination node.

Phase Lock Loop (PLL): A closed-loop feedback system used to lock the phase or frequency of the incoming signal.

Phase Shift Keying (PSK): A digital modulation technique in which the phase of the carrier signal is modulated according to the digital signal.

PN code: A pseudo random noise-like code that is of high chip rate with excellent auto- and cross correlation properties, used as spreading codes in spread spectrum techniques.

Polarization Division Multiple Access (PDMA): A multiple access technique in which the communication resource is reused by employing antenna polarizations that are orthogonal.

Pre-Assigned Multiple Access (PAMA): A fixed assignment multiple access technique in which the communication resources, the number of users, and the user assignment remain fixed for a long time.

Process gain: The process gain of a spread spectrum system specifies the difference in the performance of the system when employing the SS technique and when not using SS technique. It is usually given as the ratio of the chip rate to the data rate.

Pseudo noise sequence: A digital signal with very high frequency and very large periodicity.

Pulsed FM: An SS technique in which a linear sweep signal is used to modulate the carrier, which is then used for spreading.

Q

Quadrature Amplitude Modulation (QAM): An M-ary digital modulation technique in which the amplitude and the phase of the signal are modulated by using quadrature carrier signals.

Quadratic Phase Shift Keying (QPSK): A form of M-ary digital modulation technique in which the phases of the basis functions are in quadrature.

Quaternary PSK: An M-ary phase shift keying digital modulation technique that makes use of quadrature carrier signals to modulate the digital signal.

R

Random Assigned Multiple Access (RAMA): A multiple access technique in which the communication resource is randomly accessed by multiple users. This may result in collision when more than one user tries to transmit at the same time.

Real-time clock synchronization: Synchronization that takes care that all the systems and nodes within a time zone have the same real-time clock.

S

Shannon theorem: Shannon's theorem states that it is possible to devise a method in which a communication system will transmit information with an arbitrarily small probability of error provided that the information rate R is less than or equal to C, the channel capacity.

Soft-decision decoding: A type of decoding in which only the error probabilities may be specified rather than characterizing the decision as correct or incorrect.

Space Division Multiple Access (SDMA): A multiple access technique in which the communication resource is reused, taking advantage of the different spatial location of the users.

Spectrum: The frequency domain representation of a time domain signal that specifies the band of frequencies that the signal occupies.

Spread spectrum: The technique in which a narrow-band data signal is spread in spectrum using a code signal that is of high rate compared to the data signal data rate.

Spread spectrum technique: A modulating technique that ensures secrecy in data communication by multiplying a signal (modulated or unmodulated) with a pseudonoise sequence so that the signal is spread over a very large bandwidth.

Spreading code: The pseudo random code of high chip rate that is used to spread the spectrum of the low data rate digital signal.

Symbol synchronization: Clock timing recovery that specifies the sampling decision time instant in a correlator or matched filter receiver.

Synchronous Digital Hierarchy (SDH): A broadband transmission standard adopted by network operators for backbone transmission network.

T

Time Division Multiplexing (TDM): A technique in which signals from different transmitters are sent with the same carrier frequency but in different allotted time slots.

Time Division Multiple Access (TDMA): A multiple access technique in which the time is divided into slots and each slot is given to a particular user, enabling all the users to access the common communication resource.

Time-Hopped Spread Spectrum (THSS): An SS technique in which the high bit rate spreading code is used to determine when the data signal will be on and when it will be off.

Transponder: The communication equipment onboard the satellite that is responsible for frequency translation of the uplink signal to the downlink signal.

Traveling Wave Tube Amplifier (TWTA): A high-power amplifier operating at microwave frequency.

U

Up-converter: The up-converter accepts the modulated IF (intermediate frequency) carrier and translates its IF frequency to the uplink RF (radio frequency) frequency in the uplink frequency spectrum of the satellite. The up converter in a satellite link is usually accomplished in a dual conversion process.

V

Voltage Control Oscillator (VCO): An essential part of the PLL that produces an output frequency dependent on the input voltage.

V-SAT system: Usually designed to operate with antennas that are the equivalent of 1.8 m diameters or less. The relatively low gain of V-SAT has to be countered by a careful design.

Bibliography

Bibliography

Cooper, George R. and Clare D. McGille. *Modern Communications and Spread Spectrum*. New York: McGraw-Hill, 1986.

Ha, Tri. T. *Digital Satellite Communications*. McGraw-Hill, 1990.

Kihara, Masami, Sadayasu Ono, and Pekka Eskelinen. *Digital Clocks for Synchronization and Communications*. Boston: Artech House, 2003.

Kolimbiris, Harold. *Digital Communication Systems*. Prentice Hall, 1999.

Proakis, John G. *Digital Communications*. Boston: McGraw-Hill, 2001.

Rappaport, Theodore S. *Wireless Communications*. Upper Saddle River, NJ: Prentice Hall, 2001.

Sklar, Bernard. *Digital Communications: Fundamentals and Applications*. Englewood Cliffs, NJ: Prentice Hall, 2001.

Stallings, William. *Cryptography and Network Security*. Prentice Hall, 2003.

Xiong, Fuqin. *Digital Modulation Techniques*. Boston: Artech House, 2000.

Ziemer, Rodger E. and Roger L. Peterson. *Introduction to Digital Communication*. Upper Saddle River, NJ: Prentice Hall, 2001.

Index

Appendix

Reference to Colored Figures

Lab Exercise 2

Circuit Diagram (in Commsim)

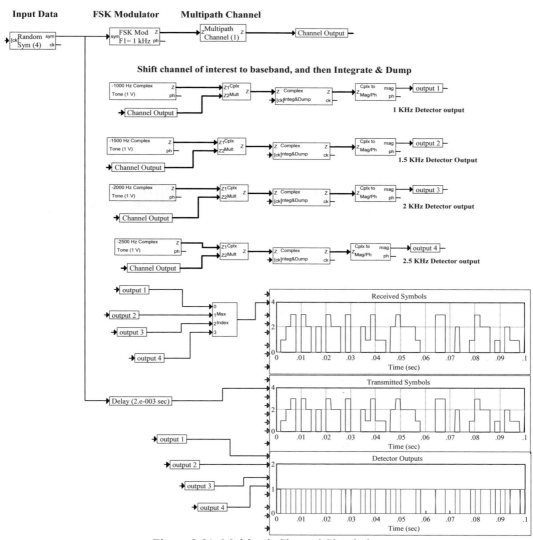

Figure 2.01: Multipath Channel Simulation

Lab Exercise 4

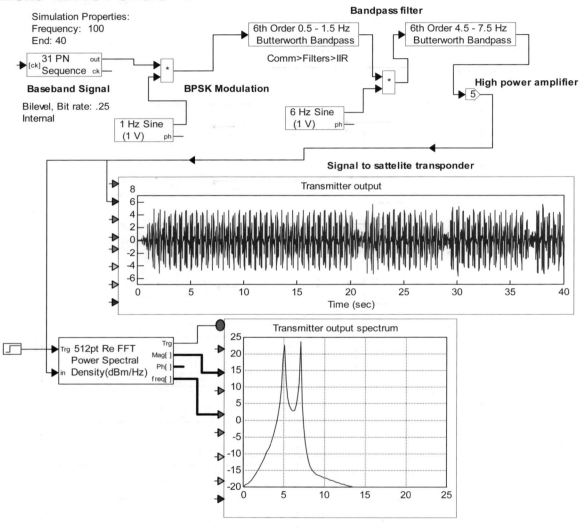

Simulation Properties:
Frequency: 100
End: 40

Bandpass filter

31 PN
[ck] Sequence out ck

6th Order 0.5 - 1.5 Hz
Butterworth Bandpass

Comm>Filters>IIR

6th Order 4.5 - 7.5 Hz
Butterworth Bandpass

Baseband Signal

BPSK Modulation

Bilevel, Bit rate: .25
Internal

High power amplifier

1 Hz Sine
(1 V) ph

6 Hz Sine
(1 V) ph

5

Signal to sattelite transponder

Transmitter output

Time (sec)

Trg 512pt Re FFT
Power Spectral
in Density(dBm/Hz)

Trg
Mag[ ]
Ph[ ]
freq[ ]

Transmitter output spectrum

Figure 4.01: Satellite Earth Station Transmitter

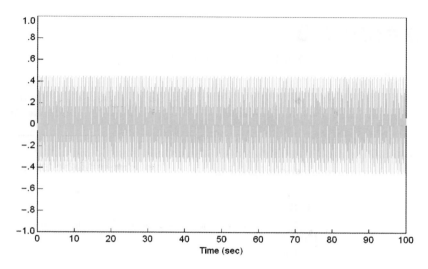

Figure 4.11: Output After Up-conversion

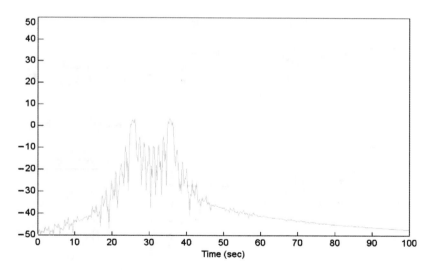

Figure 4.12: Spectrum of Up-converted Output

Lab Exercise 5

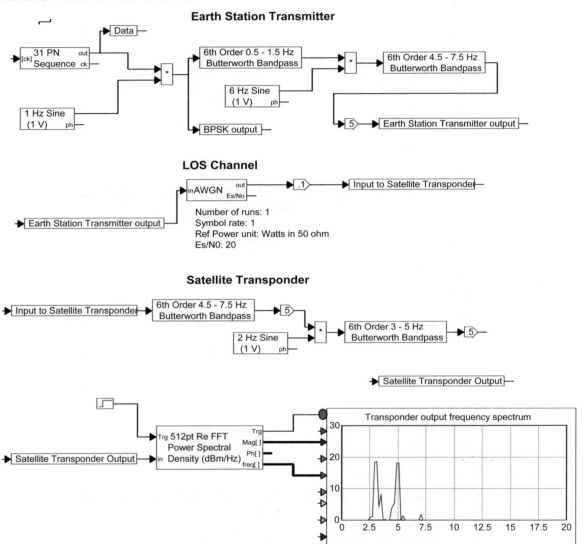

Figure 5.01: Satellite Transponder System

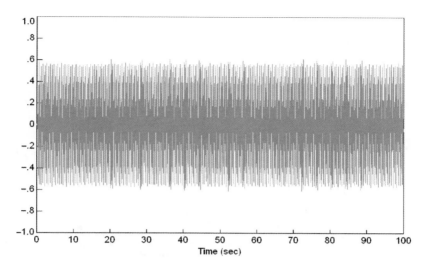

Figure 5.07: Amplifier Output of Transponder

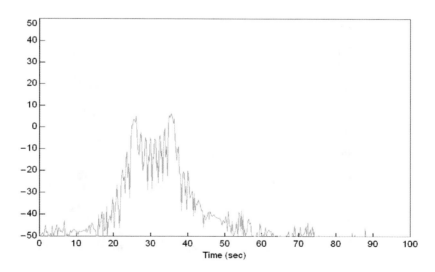

Figure 5.08: Spectrum Output of Amplifier

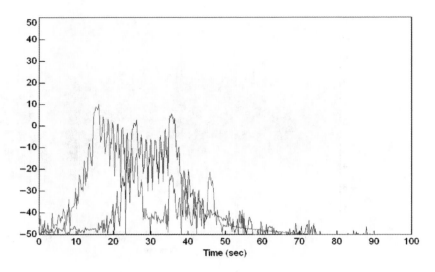

Figure 5.17: Comparison of Transponder Input and Output Spectral Regions

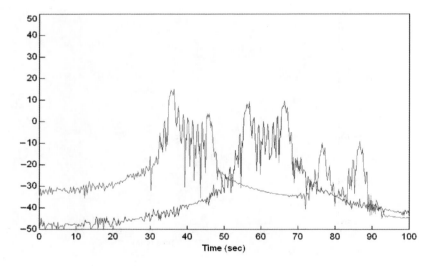

Figure 5.18: Spectral Separation for Different Sets of Frequencies

Lab Exercise 6

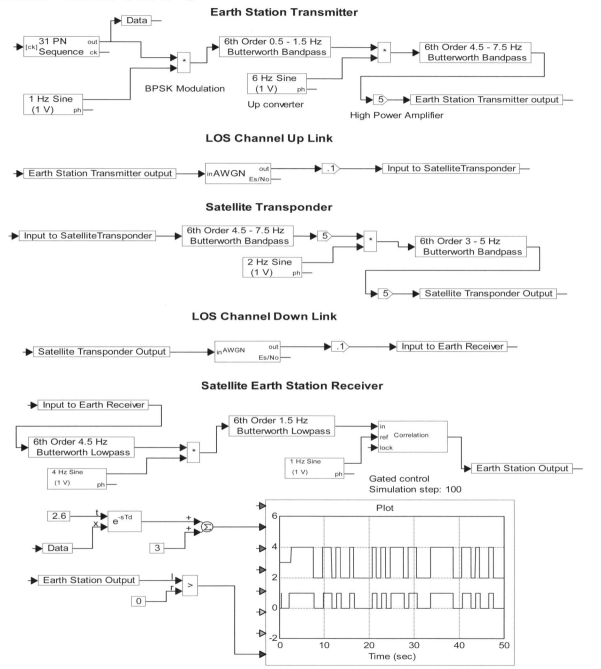

Figure 6.01: Satellite Earth Station Receiver, Transmitter and the Transponder.

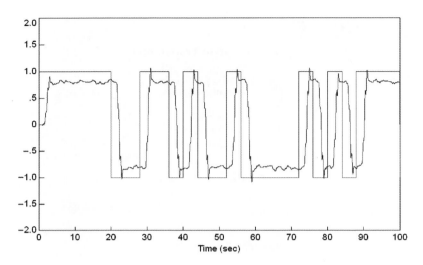

Figure 6.19: Comparison Between Scaled Correlator Output and Original Baseband Signal

Lab Exercise 7

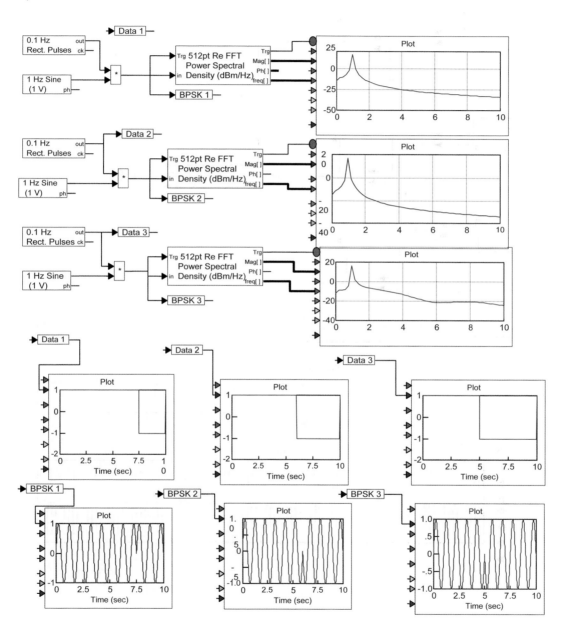

Figure 7.01: BPSK Modulator

Lab Exercise 8

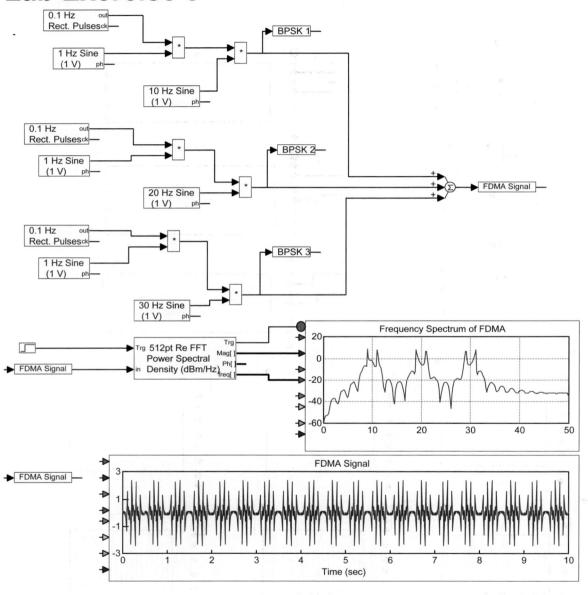

Figure 8.01: FDMA System

Lab Exercise 9

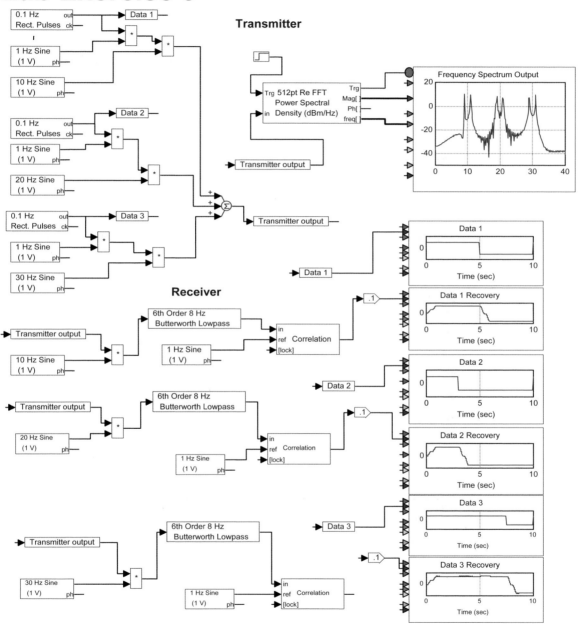

Figure 9.01: FDMA Transmitter and the Receiver System with BPSK Modulation

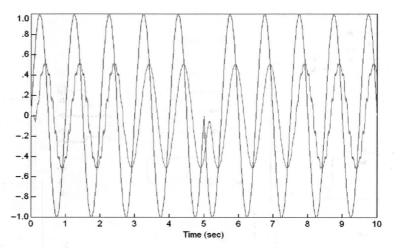

Figure 9.05: Recovered First Down-Converted Low Pass-Filtered Signal, 10Hz Channel, Compared to Original First BPSK Signal

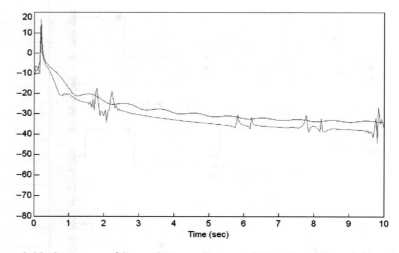

Figure 9.09: Spectrum of Second Down-Converted Low Pass-Filtered Signal, 20Hz Channel, Compared With Second BPSK Signal Spectrum

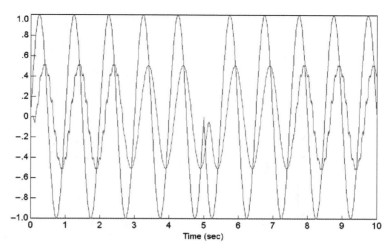

Figure 9.10: Recovered Second Down-Converted Low Pass-Filtered Signal: 20Hz Channel in Comparison with the Original Second BPSK Signal (Blue = Original)

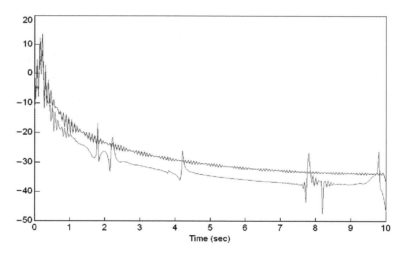

Figure 9.14: Spectrum of Third Down-Converted Low Pass-Filtered Signal, 30Hz Channel, Compared with Third BPSK Signal Spectrum

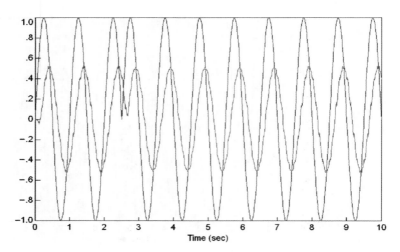

Figure 9.15: Recovered Third Down-Converted Low Pass-Filtered Signal, 30Hz Channel, Compared with Original Third BPSK Signal

Lab Exercise 10

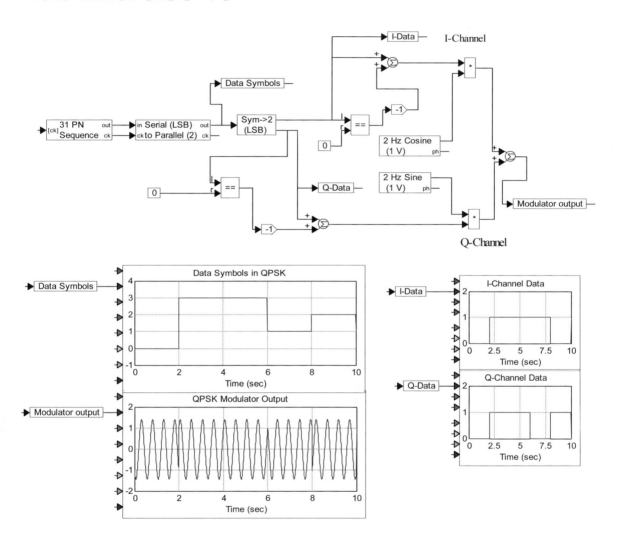

Figure 10.02: QPSK Modulator

Lab Exercise 11

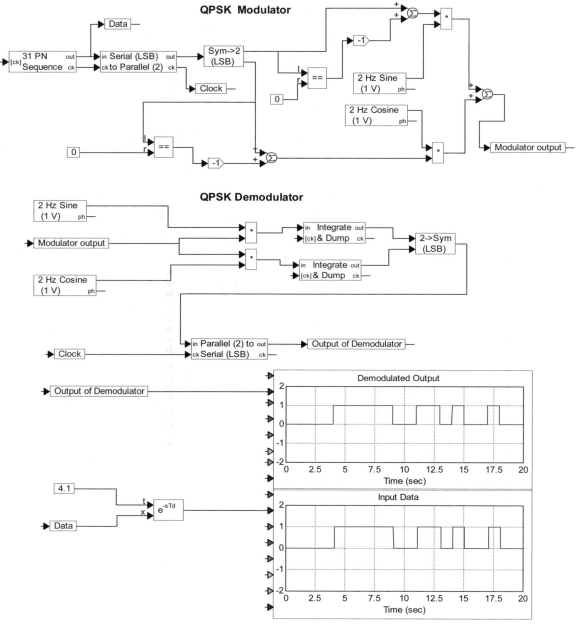

Figure 11.02: QPSK Modulation and Demodulation System

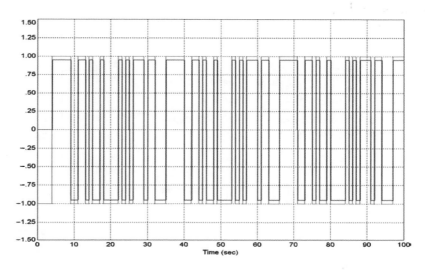

Figure 11.12: Comparison of Original Digital Signal and Signal Recovered at the Demodulator

Lab Exercise 12

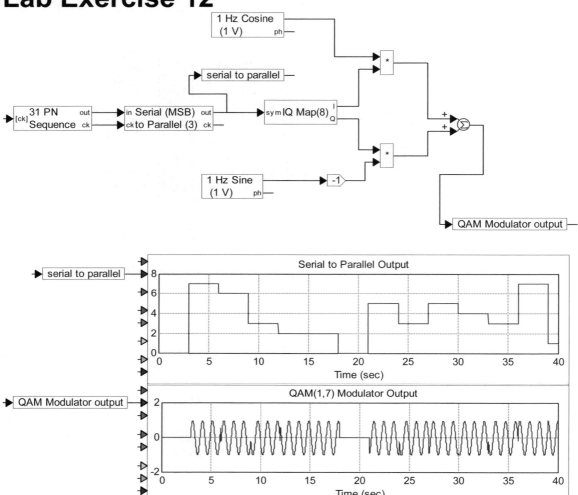

Figure 12.01: QAM Modulator

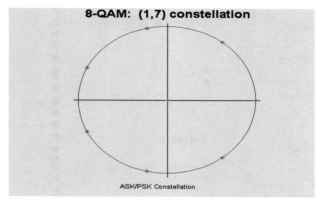

Figure 12.02: 8-QAM (1, 7) Constellation Diagram

Lab Exercise 17

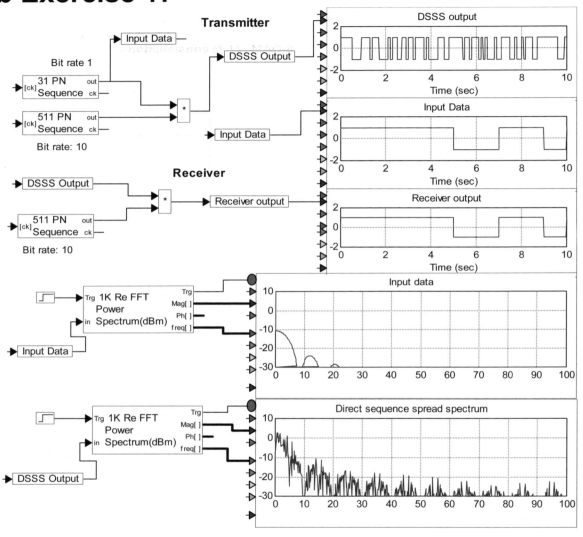

Figure 17.01: Baseband DSSS Transmitter and Receiver System

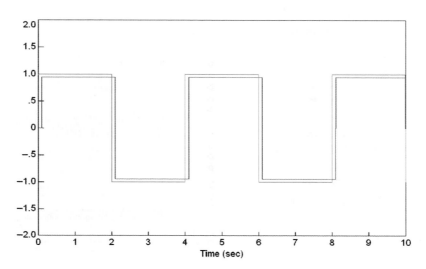

Figure 17.08: Digital Data Recovered at DSSS Receiver Using Correct PN Code Compared to Encoded Digital Data

Lab Exercise 18

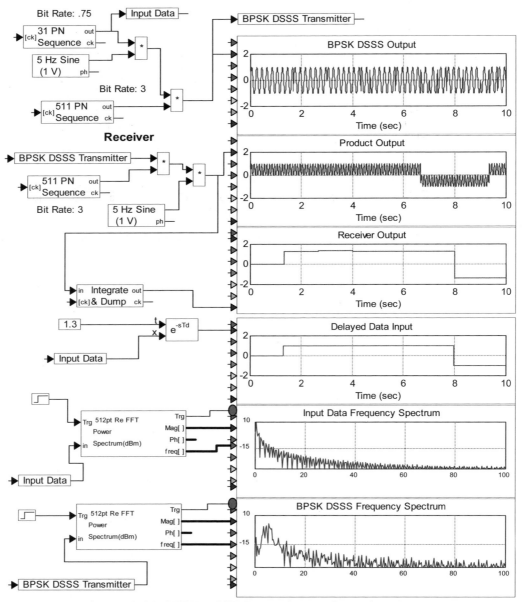

Figure 18.01: BPSK DSSS Transmitter and Receiver System